WESTERN CAPE SANDVELD FLOWERS

*Thank God
for the
Wild Flowers*

Buck Bay homestead

WESTERN CAPE SANDVELD FLOWERS

ILLUSTRATED BY
HILDA MASON A.R.C.A.

TEXT BY
ENID DU PLESSIS M.Sc. AND
COLLABORATORS

C. STRUIK (PTY) LTD · CAPE TOWN
1972

C. STRUIK (PTY) LTD.
AFRICANA SPECIALIST AND PUBLISHER

FIRST EDITION 1972

ISBN 0 86977 015 2

Lithographic Reproductions: Messrs Hirt and Carter
Designed, printed and bound by
Gothic Printing Co. Ltd., Epping, Cape, Republic of South Africa

FOREWORD   It is a great honour to be asked to write a foreword to Hilda Mason's *Western Cape Sandveld Flowers*.

Hilda Mason is well known as an artist of no mean ability, whose love of the veld has caused her to turn her hand to the botanical field of painting. Her book shows the outstanding accuracy of her drawings and choice of colours.

The members of the Darling Wild Flower Society have over the years been encouraged to preserve various areas on their farms for their lovely flowers; they have been encouraged also to fertilize and bush-cut these areas, and to make roads, so that the flowers may be accessible to the motoring public. Members of the public have shown nothing but appreciation. Gone is the day when they could be stigmatized as 'locusts', when they stripped the veld of its beauty by injudicious picking.

The authorities have been terrific in helping to spread the gospel of "Save the flowers", and in implementing the laws provided to save our natural heritage.

The interest generated by the Darling Wild Flowers Shows (which have become an annual institution) has led members to believe that most of the flowers recorded and illustrated by the earlier botanists such as Thunberg and Bolus, are still with us. We now realize that the veld is a living entity with flowers in it throughout the year; people have only to look for them.

We have appreciated only recently that many of the most beautiful flowers appear at odd times, and it is necessary to know both where and when to find them.

Hilda has been greatly assisted in her work by her botanist friend Enid du Plessis, who has given her lots of encouragement and much valuable assistance. Other botanical friends have also collaborated in helping to produce what is a wonderful work and a lasting record for future generations.

FREDERICK DUCKITT.

Waylands, Darling,

May 1972

PUBLISHER'S NOTE   The publishers and author wish to express their thanks to Mr H. F. Oppenheimer and the Cape Tercentenary Foundation, who both made a generous grant-in-aid towards the cost of reproducing the many illustrations in colour. Without their support this publication would not have been possible in its present form.

ACKNOWLEDGEMENT   I acknowledge my gratitude to Enid du Plessis for her inspiration, enthusiasm, energy and partnership in this book. I am indebted to many friendly helpers and farmers who helped in the search for the wild flowers illustrated and described here. Firstly do I mention the wonderful Duckitt family, especially Mrs Duckitt Snr, and Frederick and Wilferd and their wives, who have been so largely responsible for the preservation of the wild flowers of the Darling district, who found specimens for me, and so hospitably entertained me during Darling Flower Shows. My deep thanks are due too to Mr and Mrs Martin Melck, Mr and Mrs Brian Lello, Mr and Mrs Willem Basson, Mr and Mrs Otto Blankenberg, Mr Nico Blankenberg, Mr and Mrs F. Schwabe, Mr and Mrs van Breda and Mrs E. Steyn, who gave me access to their lands and produced the rare species known only to themselves. My thanks also to the director of Nature Conservation of the Cape Province for permission to collect the necessary specimens. I remember Mr and Mrs Harold Krumm for their assistance – and many others too numerous to mention.

I also want to thank the director of Nature Conservation of the Cape Peninsula for his permission to collect the necessary specimens.

The identification of the flowers has been made by specialists, some now working far afield: Miss W. F. Barker and staff, Dr J. P. Rourke, Mr Walter Wisura, Kirstenbosch; Mr E. H. Oliver, Prof. M. P. de Vos, Miss M. Thompson, Stellenbosch; Prof. T. T. Barnard, Cape Town; Mr W. Marais at Kew; Prof. E. Schelpe and Miss Elsie Esterhuizen, Mr H. Tölken, Dr P. Goldblatt, Bolus Herbarium; Dr I. Verdoorn and Mrs A. A. Mauve, Botanical Research Institute, Pretoria; Dr R. Dahlgren, Uppsala, Sweden.

CONTENTS

Foreword

Preface

Introduction

PREFACE 'Do you like flowers?', 'Have you always painted?' These were the questions that started this book. It was the idea of Enid du Plessis (then information officer at the National Botanic Gardens Kirstenbosch) that I should record the flowers of the Sandveld and coastal strip of the Western Cape Province before it was destroyed by growing industrialization, townships, and man.

It was in March 1969 that the first five paintings were approved and I set out with the blessing of the conservation authorities to search the sandy areas along the coast, north of Blouberg, for any flower that I could find and paint. The spring flowers came in August that year, but after three weeks the lack of further rain and hot dry winds seared the countryside and caused the area to be officially proclaimed as drought-stricken. The Darling Wild Flower Show had to be cancelled. There *were* a few flowers, but only here and there, and they were smaller than usual. What there were, however, I collected and painted; and the dried specimens went to the Kirstenbosch Herbarium for identification. I had much to learn. I very quickly discovered that the little flies called *miggies*, which breed in the vleis, make painting out of doors almost impossible, and that the horse-flies are even worse. Then I had to learn how to care for the flowers so that they would keep long enough for me to draw and paint them. Some wilt almost immediately – especially those from plants with a woody stem. Every flower has its own built-in mechanism, actuated by the sun, heat, or simply time of day. The irises open only at midday and close again after three or four hours; and each flower lasts but a day. Some flowers open in the evening, others early and close early, while many spread their perfumes only at night.

It was always exciting to find, when one's studio was bathed in a delicious perfume, that it was often the smallest and most inconspicuous flower that was responsible. Many flowers will open only on sunny days; most dislike the south-east wind; and the spring flowers usually face and follow the sun as it crosses the sky. There are a few flowers that open in any weather and any temperature and usually to a set time; it is most interesting and mystifying. Most spring flowers have their special season cycle, and if the weather is not right for them they will not flower at all, but wait for the next year. The immense variety of form and colour and pattern is indescribable. Some plants have their own small insects, so tiny that they are seen only with a magnifying glass, but they run around at great speed. An exciting new world opened to me – and every day was different.

The collecting and painting occupied me fully for about two and a half years. I travelled many miles, often alone but also on excursions with botanists, who knew where to find the rarer species, and sometimes with my husband Eric, who gave up his time to join several excursions of a week or so to the more northerly places, and more often in and around Langebaan. He was of immense help, being a trained observer and possessing the patience for this demanding occupation. He also wrote most of the introduction.

HILDA MASON.
Newlands, Cape,
June 1972

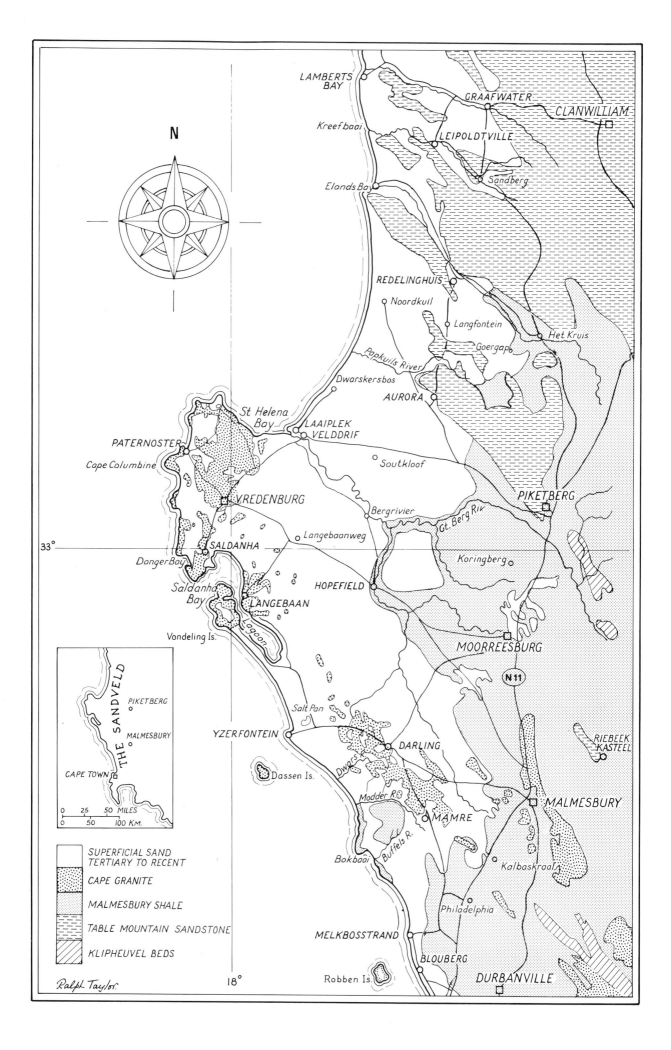

N

LAMBERTS BAY
GRAAFWATER
CLANWILLIAM
Kreefbaai
LEIPOLDTVILLE
Sandberg
Elands Bay
REDELINGHUIS
Noordkuil
Langfontein
Het Kruis
Goergap
Popkuils River
Dwarskersbos
AURORA
St Helena Bay
LAAIPLEK
VELDDRIF
PATERNOSTER
Soutkloof
Cape Columbine
VREDENBURG
PIKETBERG
Bergrivier
Gt. Berg Riv
33°
SALDANHA
Langebaanweg
Danger Bay
Koringberg
Saldanha Bay
HOPEFIELD
LANGEBAAN
Lagoon
Vondeling Is.
MOORREESBURG
Salt Pan
N 11
YZERFONTEIN
DARLING
RIEBEEK
KASTEEL
Dwars
Dassen Is.
Modder R
MALMESBURY
MAMRE
Buffels R.
Kalbaskraal
Bokbaai
Philadelphia
MELKBOSSTRAND
BLOUBERG
Robben Is.
DURBANVILLE

THE SANDVELD

PIKETBERG

MALMESBURY

CAPE TOWN

| 0 | 25 | 50 MILES |
| 0 | 50 | 100 KM. |

SUPERFICIAL SAND
TERTIARY TO RECENT

CAPE GRANITE

MALMESBURY SHALE

TABLE MOUNTAIN SANDSTONE

KLIPHEUVEL BEDS

Ralph Taylor.

18°

INTRODUCTION ## The Sandveld: Early Visitors

The first Europeans to visit any part of the Sandveld – which for the purpose of this book is regarded as that strip of the coast of the western Cape Province which extends from Blouberg to Elands Bay – were Vasco da Gama and his companions in 1497. A journalist of the expedition recorded that at St. Helena Bay the climate was temperate, the land was healthy, and there were 'good plants'. The local inhabitants, who were Bushmen, ate the roots of certain of these plants, which were sampled by one of the Portuguese.

But the Sandveld lay away from the sailing routes between Europe and India, and though a Portuguese writer early in the sixteenth century was able to comment on, and eulogize, the flora of the Cape Peninsula, he had nothing to say about the coast to the north. In fact, nothing is known of this area until 1601, when a Netherlander, Joris van Spilbergen, made a coasting, and mis-called a large bay which he observed Saldanha, a name which had rightly belonged to Table Bay.

English ships began to visit Saldanha. In 1612, it is known, one Captain Samuel Castleton anchored in the bay. He sent a ship's boat in search of water, and Hottentots guided the seamen to what was no more than 'a little puddle', he complained; he added, 'this Country seemed to be a very barren place'.

In 1623 a Dane, Jon Olafsson, anchored off what was later to be known as Skapen Island for fourteen days, during which time he careened his ship and fished. But he and French and English masters who visited the bay were more interested in whales and their oil and sea-lions and their pelts than unremunerative flora.

In October 1648 Etienne de Flacourt, Director-General of the French East India Company in Madagascar, anchored off Cormorant Island, the present Meeuw, at the entrance to Flamingo inlet, i.e. Riet Bay. His men took in water at the foot of a hill which he ascended 'to view all this land', and take note of what it produced. He recorded 'all the soil of these islands, and of the mainland in these regions, is very good, and would produce everything if it were cultivated. For the most part it is all black earth and is all covered with the verdure of various sorts of flowering plants and of bushes: there are no large trees'. He commented that certain areas were well manured by elephants and other animals.

In 1652, only seven months after founding a settlement at Table Bay, Jan van Riebeeck sent a vessel to Saldanha and St. Helena bays in search of profit. The commander landed some sheep on what was thereafter called Skapen Island, where he found 2 700 cured sea-lion skins, neatly stacked by a French expedition. The island was 'very stony and overgrown with asparagus (but of a better kind) as well as other scrubs and thorns'. The commander described the shore of the bay as being very dry and sandy, and covered with sharp rushes. He ascended a high hill; 'the country seemed to be completely barren, covered with prickly shrubs'. But 'the country is quite good during the green season'. Twice French expeditions sought to annex the Saldanha Bay area, but from 1676 military posts protected the claims of the Netherlands East India Company.

Meanwhile there had been Netherlands overland exploration northwards from Table Bay. In 1655 Jan Wintervogel, who had explored in Brazil, reached the area of later Malmesbury. On his return he left behind 'one Jan de Vos, who died from eating too many bitter almonds'. Four years later Christian Janssen set out, required to report, among other instructions, on the nature of the soil – whether, for instance, it was arable, sandy or stony – and on edible fruits and root crops. But he travelled in February and March, and 'found the country everywhere so barren, parched and ill-supplied with pasturage and water that they were forced to turn back'; he and his men reached the lower Berg River. The next year Jan Danckaert, taking a more easterly route, east of Riebeeck Kasteel and Piketberg, discovered the Olifants River and reached the area of later Clanwilliam. In February 1661 a party under Van Meerhoff crossed the Olifants River near Graafwater and made contact with Nama people who were in the habit, like the Hottentots nearer Table Bay, of burning the veld to secure pasture for their cattle; 'as far as the country is concerned it is nothing but sand-dunes over-grown with underwood and thorn-bushes'. In December of that year Pieter Everaerts discovered the mouth of the Olifants River and penetrated further into the Sandveld, towards later Nuwerus. North-wards, he reported to Van Riebeeck, the soil was 'as dry as a plank and is nothing but sand dotted with molehills. There is neither foliage nor grass there, nothing but an occasional puddle of muddy water, so brackish that its edges are encrusted with white salt'.

The first scientist known to enter the Sandveld was Wilhelmus Ten Rhyne, a physician, who had been employed by the Netherlands East India Company in Japan and Batavia, who in 1673 visited the Cape and Saldanha Bay and collected and described a number of plants.

Olof Bergh, a Swede in the employ of the Company in 1682 and again in 1683, explored towards the copper fields of Namaqualand. On his second journey he was accompanied by Hendrik Claudius, an artist and apothecary, whose sketches of plants attracted the attention of commissary H. A. van Rheede, a noted botanist, who authorized governor Simon van der Stel to discover the copper mountains. Claudius accompanied the expedition, which left Cape Town at the end of August, 1685. On the fifth day the expedition reached 'a high hill, up which we marched, the top thickly grown with low scrub in the hollows, and with a very pleasant valley sown by Nature with flowers of all colours and with abundance of grass to delight the beholder'. In the Berg River valley 'the herb called Prei in Holland grew wild in such abundance that all the plain was filled with its scent'. Beyond the Piketberg the expedition dropped to the Sandveld, through hills 'all of sand and rocky soils, densely grown with bush and the valleys full of reeds, very lonely and dismal'. Beyond lay sand-dunes, over-grown with dense scrub. It was grass that the guides were looking for rather than flowers, but Claudius collected a number of plants which he described and illustrated.

Exploration northwards was promptly followed by occupation. The Company in 1701 established a military post at the aptly named Groenkloof (which Moravian missionaries, who established themselves there in 1808, were later to rename Mamre). Also from 1701 occur references to grazing farms in the Swartland, which doubtless obtained its name from the dense cover of dark green bush in what was later to be known as the Malmesbury district.

Peter Kolb, a German, visited the Cape early in the eighteenth century and, though he ventured no further afield than Mamre to the north and the site of Caledon to the east, he had much to say about the natural history of the Cape. He admitted (to quote from an English translation of his work published in 1731) 'I am but little skilled in Botanic Descriptions. My Botanic reader will pardon me then where I am defective in Point of Art, and be satisfied with my Industry to oblige him when Genius and Method fail me'. Thanks largely to assistance from Jan Hartog, the Company's gardener, he was able to catalogue close on four hundred species – many of which came from the Groenkloof area.

Kolb was particularly interested in the customs of the Hottentots. He declared that they gathered a root called Kanna which they held in much great esteem: 'they look upon it as the greatest Chearer of the Spirits, and noblest Restorative in the World. They will give almost any thing in Exchange for it; and will, any of them, run Twenty Miles upon an Errand, or perform a hard Day's Work, for a very small Bit of it'. It is doubtful, however, whether this *Sceletium anatomicum* came from the Sandveld. The Hottentots knew many medicinal plants, and for most ailments took powders or infusions of wild sage, fennel, garlic, wild figs or buchu. The juice of certain aloe-leaves was 'a good Cathartic, and at the same time an excellent Stomachic'.

Kolb wrote of the *Arum aethiopicum*: 'It grows, for the most Part, in the Marshes; and yields a white Flower, of an agreable Smell. The Root is white and large; and, when cut in Slices, is, to the Eye, so like *Spanish*-Raddish, that a Man, who is acquainted with that Root, would not easily, by looking upon it, take it for any thing else. This great Resemblance, to the Eye, between the two Roots, frequently draws the CAPE-*Europeans*, for the Sake of a little Diversion, to put the *Arum aethiopicum* upon Strangers for *Spanish*-Raddish, And the Effect of that Arum upon the palate, is so very tormenting, that the Mirth of this Deceit is frequently spoil'd by the Resentment of the Deceiv'd. For that Root stings and enflames the Mouth to such a Degree, that the Torment is hardly to be endur'd. And the taking of Water in the Mouth, to allay it (which a Stranger is tempted to do) enrages it'.

Kolb continued: 'The Root of the *Arum*, among the CAPE-*Europeans*, is ordinarily called *Hottentot*-Bread; the *Hottentots* frequently eating it in the Place of Bread. They boil out its Acrimony in two or three fresh Waters, and then dry it in the Sun. Afterwards they roast it in Embers. And thus 'tis fitted to their Palates.'

As the eighteenth century wore on more and more farms came to be allocated in the present Malmesbury and Piketberg districts, such as Gansekraal in 1709, Teefontein in 1716, Karnmelke Fontein (now Waylands) by 1719, Hendrik Oostwald Eksteen's farm on Langebaan lagoon in 1729, and Kersefontein, on the lower Berg River, in 1744, named presumably after the wild-cherry bush. But agriculture had stripped only an insignificant proportion of the vegetation of the Sandveld by the time that the great collectors arrived in the area towards the end of the eighteenth century.

In 1772 there came to the Cape the Swedish physician, Carl Thunberg, whom Professor MacOwan (in his presidential address to the South African Philosophical Society in 1886) described as 'a man truly worthy to be called the Father of Cape Botany'; and, he added, 'as long as in our paradise of flowers there wanders a single botanist so long will the name of Thunberg be held in honoured remembrance'. Thunberg made three notable journeys. On the first he was accompanied by Johan Auge, the Company's gardener, who had already made eighteen journeys into the interior. The party left Cape Town on 7 September 1772. The first day Thunberg remarked on the Protea hypophylla, seen 'creeping and procumbent'. He remained a week at Groenkloof, 'this pleasant place', collecting. 'The sandy and low plains, which we traversed, abounded at this time in bulbous plants, besides others which were now sprung up in consequence of the heavy rains that had fallen during the winter, and which with their infinitely varied flowers decorated these otherwise naked heaths'. He noted that the bulbs of the *Iris edulis*, when boiled and served at table, tasted much like potatoes. The seed vessels of a species of euphorbia, pulverized, were used for poisoning jackals and here he saw the castor oil plant, the seeds of which were boiled, and the oil skimmed off, to be used as a gentle purge. Moreover, the leaves of the shrub dried, and applied to the head, were 'affirmed to be serviceable in the headach'.

Thunberg continued to Saldanha Bay, noticing on the way that the expressed juice of the sow thistle (*Sonchus oleraceus*) was used in the treatment of ulcers. 'The *Albuca major* grew in this neighbourhood, tall, straight, and elegant. Its succulent stalk, which is rather mucilaginous, is chewed by the Hottentots and their travellers, by way of quenching their thirst'. On the islands in Saldanha Bay grass grew in abundance. He returned to Teefontein. 'Great complaints were made of the seed-vessels of the *Rumex spinosus* (dubelties), which grew very common here, as the sharp prickles of them cut the feet of the slaves and others, who walked bare-footed'. In wet years, 'the *Pharnaceum mollugo* (muggekruyd) grows copiously here, and is said to make the cattle that feed on it, very fat'. And he commented on a bush the black berries of which were greedily devoured by crows.

Thunberg continued to the Berg River. 'The root of anise (*Anys wortel*) was eaten here roasted, and tasted well; it is either roasted in the embers, or boiled in milk, or else stewed with meat. The farmers sometimes make their slaves dig up a large quantity of them, which they sell in town'. The root of the '*gatagay*' was also roasted in the embers and eaten, but this had 'a bad and disagreeable taste'. As he entered the Tulbagh valley he commented on the 'tintirinties' which was 'a name given to a species of *Ornithogalum*', with a white flower, from the sound it produced, when two stalks of it were rubbed against each other'. At the end of his journey, which took him as far east as the Gamtoos River, he discoursed on the medicinal plants of the Cape – numbers of which came from the Sandveld.

On his second journey Thunberg was accompanied by Francis Masson, a gardener sent out by King George III of England to collect plants and seeds for the royal gardens at Kew. North of Blouberg, Thunberg noted that the roots of fennel were roasted and eaten in the same way as those of anise.

The slaves of a farm he visited collected great quantities of the bulbs of the *Iris edulis*, 'a plant which grew here in abundance, and decorated the fields with a variety of white, yellow and blue flowers'. He repeated that these bulbs were roasted, boiled or stewed with milk, 'and appeared to me to be both palatable and nourishing'. Beyond Groenkloof he commented on the deep sand and the 'downs' which made the roads grievously heavy for the oxen which drew his cart and Masson's wagon. At Gansekraal he remarked that Hottentots were collecting buchu. This they dried first in the shade, then over a fire, before pulverizing it. With the powder they dusted themselves or prepared an ointment with which they smeared their bodies and gave themselves an odour, which to Thunberg (but presumably not to themselves) was rank, fetid and disagreeable. In the Saldanha area Thunberg recorded 'it is only in the spring and in the beginning of summer, that these low sandy plains are adorned with flowers'; once the south-east winds and drought had set in the seeds of the flowers were rapidly scattered over the veld. There were thickets in the sandy plains, but they consisted solely of slender shrubs from four to six feet high.

The travellers tried to reach Martin Melck's farm, Kersefontein, but could not cross the Berg River because of its height, and made a detour up the Sout River towards the Swartland which now boasted a church of its own and an increasing population. Travelling northwards again, Thunberg noted that 'the *Cyanella capensis* (Raapuyntjes), a kind of onion, was roasted for the table of the farmers'; and that 'the *Viscum aethiopicum* was used in diarrhoeas, and also for tea'. From the Piketberg area the travellers climbed to the Bokkeveld and headed eastwards.

Thunberg and Masson set out again together in 1774. They left Cape Town at the end of September, and in the middle of October found themselves below Piketberg. 'Here grew a shrub called Zand-olyve (*Dodonea angustifolia*), the wood of which was of a hard nature. This was dried, and a decoction of it was drank in fevers, by way of a purgative. Here too was found the *Stapelia incarnata*, 'a very branchy plant without leaves', which the Hottentots ate after peeling off the edges and prickles. The travellers followed the Verlooren valley, where the reeds and rushes were often so high that the water-course could not be seen. They reached its mouth, 'in a sandy and barren field, where no colonists dwelt'. They travelled northwards, up the exhausting sandy plain, scraping past bushes covered in transparent brittle prickles, and discovering a rare *Codon royeni*. They came to the welcome coolness of the Heerenlogement, where they observed the names of previous travellers on the walls of the cave. They continued to the Olifants River, before heading eastwards and climbing the mountain barrier, observing on the way the *Aloe dichotoma*, the stem of which, hollowed out, provided the Hottentot with his quiver.

Francis Masson, who had already made one journey eastwards before he joined forces with Thunberg, left only a brief account of his three journeys. He, like his companion, commented of his journey to Saldanha Bay in 1773, 'we travelled over a deep sandy country with great fatigue'. While at Saldanha Bay he recorded, on 22 September, 'We found here a great variety of curious plants; and in particular a large bulbous root growing on dry precipices which the Dutch call vergift-boll, poison bulb, the juice of which they say the Hottentots use as an ingredient to poison their arrows. We found it to be a species of *Amaryllis* and, by the leaves growing in a fan shape, we called it *Amaryllis disticha*'. On 27 September he noted at St. Helena Bay, 'the whole country affords a fine field for botany, being enamelled with the greatest number of flowers I ever saw, of exquisite beauty and fragrance'. At the end of October 'We came to a pont or ferry where we collected a great number of beautiful plants, particularly ixiae, irides and gladioli'.

Saldanha Bay soon became more widely known in the world. The outbreak of hostilities in Europe in 1780 invested the Cape with new strategic importance. The next year a French fleet, which had surprised a British fleet at anchor in the Cape Verde Islands, landed troops at Cape Town and so forestalled a British occupation. Five merchantmen of the Netherlands East India Company hid in Saldanha Bay, but the British fleet, when it made its belated appearance, took four of them prize. In 1795 a British force succeeded in occupying the Cape. In August 1796 word reached Cape Town that a Netherlands fleet of nine ships had entered Saldanha Bay. A force of 2 500 men marched to Langebaan and a battery of guns exchanged fire with a frigate off Sandy Bay. A British fleet closed the entrance to Saldanha, and all nine ships were forced to surrender.

John Barrow, private secretary to Governor Macartney (and later to become second secretary at the British Admiralty) made extensive journeys in the colony. He was particularly concerned to know whether Saldanha Bay could be developed for naval and mercantile purposes. For such purposes fresh water and ample firewood were essential. He considered for the first a proposal to divert the waters of the Berg River, and for the second, the use of the roots of some of the local flora: 'In the sand hills, that surround a part of the bay, grow several kinds of shrubby plants, whose long and thick roots are easily drawn out of the loose sand and in such abundance, as scarcely to be credited. They form a kind of subterranean forest'.

Barrow's proposals were criticized by Dr. M. Heinrich Lichtenstein, who accompanied the commissary De Mist on a journey of inspection during the period of Batavian republic rule at the Cape. Lichtenstein considered that Barrow, talking of the 'subterranean forest' had probably been referring to the *Cussonia spicata*; but those plants took extremely long to grow and if roots were used for firewood for fleets the species would soon be destroyed.

The commissary's party proceeded north by the familiar road past Groen-kloof, where there were now thirty farms. Northwards of there he commented on the sandy places strewn with low, solitary shrubs. 'Many sorts of heath plants enlivened in a degree the dreariness of the scene: we saw several *pelar-gonias*, *gnidae*, and *passerinae*, with here and there a plant something of the lily kind, and abundance of *garteria*, *asters*, *elichrysia*, and others of the *syngenesia* class, the rays of which were even now expanded to the mid-day sun'. And to the east the chain of mountains in the distance raised their rugged heads. Teefontein he proclaimed to be one of the best spots in this sandy country, with particularly good grass for sheep and horses. 'We were here regaled with a genuine African dish, the anis root, which has a strong spicy taste, and when cooked seems extremely nourishing. It is in perfection at this time of the year, and is sometimes brought to Cape Town as a delicacy.' Lichtenstein remarked, 'extremely to my satisfaction, that these sandy downs were inhabited by insects and plants wholly appropriate to the spot, and varying extremely from those more immediately in the neighbourhood of the Cape Town'. He visited Skapen Island and noted, 'the vegetation is confined chiefly to some sorts of the *mesem-bryanthemum*, particularly the *Mesembryanthemum crystallinum*, or ice-plant as it is generally called, and some little shrubby plants'. At Springfontein he wrote, 'the shrubs, which were higher than we had generally seen, united with several sorts of *protea*, *rhus*, and other small trees, confined the prospect . . .'. The party visited Kersefontein, which Lichtenstein called Kirstenfontein, misled by the name of Kirsten, the temporary occupant, and then passed along the east bank of the Berg River, 'through a tiresome sand, but scattered over with some pretty little flowers, particularly several sorts of pelargonia but nothing like a bush high enough to afford the least shade to the traveller'.

One further traveller can be mentioned: the missionary Latrobe, who, no botanist, in December 1815, 'dragged through deep sand almost the whole way to Groenekloof. No trees, and but few shrubs, adorn the waste, but we noticed many pretty species of heath and some elegant flowers, unknown to us. The most common plant is the so-called Hottentot fig.' At night the fire was fed with rhinoceros bushes, 'a resinous plant with large roots, but easily pulled up'. Beyond Blouberg he travelled 'through a barren, sandy heath'. But, he remarked in sudden enthusiasm of the vegetation around Groenkloof, 'the waste produces some beautiful plants, among which I particularly noticed the Fahlblar, a species of aloe, the leaves of which are round, of a pale blue colour, and spreading near the ground, the stalk about a foot long and the flowers, which are bell-shaped and of a deep scarlet, hanging down in clusters'.

By now veld-clearing and burning was widespread, for agriculture was being introduced into the area. The most advanced techniques of agriculture were exercised by William Duckitt. William Duckitt had been sent from England in 1800, during the first British occupation of the Cape, to improve agriculture; he arrived at the Cape with nine assistants, some Devon cattle, a selection of seeds and plants, and equipment, including an iron plough invented by his father. In 1815 he acquired Klavervlei in the Groenkloof, where he practised scientific husbandry – and put no more than ten per cent of his vast farm under cereals. He, those who came under his influence, and his family, did much toward preserving the flora of the Sandveld.

The Sandveld: Description

'Relief features and regional differences of climate divide the Cape Province into a number of well-defined geographic regions', Professor W. J. Talbot declared in his book, *Swartland and Sandveld*. 'The westernmost division, the western lowland, is clearly delimited on the east by the sandstone scarps and rugged crests of the mountain system which, under various local names, extends northwards from the Hottentots Holland to the Olifants River Mountains. The lowland varies in width from about twenty-five miles [40 km] in the south to nearly seventy miles [112 km] in the latitude of Saldanha (33°S.). Over most of its area it is characterized by broad gently-undulating landscapes to which local variety of relief is imparted by broad granitic massifs rising to between 1 500 [457 m] and 2 500 feet [762 m] above the general level, as in the Paardeberg, and by the angular skylines of quartzitic ranges, outliers of the mountain system to the east rising locally to more than 3 000 feet [915 m] above sea level, as in the Kasteelberg.

'In geologically recent times', Professor Talbot continued, 'almost the whole of the region was covered by a shallow sea from which such granitic massifs and quartzitic ranges stood out as islands. The extensive sand deposits which today form the western and southern margins of the lowland – the Strandveld, or Sandveld, and the Cape Flats – are derived from the shallow-water and beach deposits of this sea, together with sand blown inland from the beaches in more recent times. The phosphate deposits of the Langebaan neighbourhood appear to be derived from guano deposited by sea birds on low islands in this former sea. During this period marine erosion and deposition produced below sea level gentle slopes and locally almost level surfaces while above sea level the lower slopes of the insular mountain masses were made steeper as coastal erosion cut back their bases. Later, as the region was gradually raised above sea-level, the rivers rising in the mountains extended their courses across the emerging sea floor and began to carve new valleys into it. In the present landscapes the gentle slopes of the old sea floor are still dominant. Steep slopes are of local occurrence. They are characteristic of the margins of the mountain masses, where some particularly steep slopes may represent the ruins of old sea cliffs and of the sides of the valleys which have been cut into the plain since its emergence.'

The Sandveld, in short, consists of a continuous low coastal plain of marine and aeolian sands. But 'in places these surfaces are varied by ridges and sand hills built up by the strong southerly winds. Most of these are now fixed by vegetation, although locally, in the neighbourhood of wide beaches and in formerly burnt-over areas inland, several thousand morgen are still occupied by advancing dunes. Here and there above the generally monotonous landscape the smooth slopes of granite hills and koppies emerge from beneath the mantle of sand, as in the peninsulas that embrace Saldanha Bay . . . '

The Swartland, which includes the Piketberg, 'is a region of gentle relief where erosion has truncated the highly folded slates, phyllites, quartzites, and siltstones of the Malmesbury Series forming a surface of moderate slopes with locally almost level areas, and with steeper slopes and occasional low bluffs along the river courses'. Here, too, the generally low and undulating land is broken by occasional great masses of granite, such as the Paardeberg, and of Table Mountain sandstone, such as the Kasteelberg and Piketberg.

As a consequence of this geological history there are three main types of soil in the Sandveld. There are soils from marine and alluvial beds which are fine, loosely-grained sands with low water-retaining capacity; at Hopefield these are more well-drained and dry for successful cultivation, but at Langebaan the sands have heavy limestone overlays. There are soils derived from the granites which are reddish, sandy loams, poor in nitrogen and phosphates, found for instance, in the area north of Vredenburg. And there are soils derived from the Malmesbury shales which are often shallow and consist of brown sand or gravel loams, plastic when wet and poor in nitrogen and phosphate.

The climate is one of mild and moist or wet winters, with prevailing northwesterly winds, and hot dry summers, with prevailing southerly winds. Frost is rare except on mountain slopes, but temperatures of 38°C are not unknown. Along most of the Sandveld the annual rainfall averages between 125 and 350 mm; in the Darling area and on the lower slopes of the Piketberg the range is between 250 and 500 mm; and between these areas the land receives between 250 and 280 mm. Virtually all the rain falls between April and September. But these are average falls – and there are 'good' years and 'bad' years. 'In September and October, lengthening days, rising temperatures, and soils still moist from winter rains and late showers stimulate a great outburst of vegetative activity. The veld, grey-green and brown at other seasons, becomes brilliant with wild flowers.'

The Sandveld: Vegetation

In 1953 Mr J. P. H. Acocks published a most usable classification of South African vegetation into recognisable veld types. Since his work was meant primarily as a practical guide to farmers, his definition of veld type was 'a unit of vegetation whose range of variation is small enough to permit the whole of it to have the same farming potentialities'.

The flora of the Sandveld was not well known, but Acocks recognized three veld types. Coastal macchia is confined to unconsolidated sands and Malmesbury shale on the west and south western coast in areas which have not been extensively ploughed, ranging in altitude between sea-level and 300 m and with a rainfall between 275 and 500 mm per year. Acocks speculated that the climax of this type may be grass and open scrub. Coastal renosterveld is found on clay derived from weathered granite, in areas similar in altitude and rainfall to that of the coastal macchia, but because of extensive ploughing there are only relics of the natural vegetation. The natural climax he speculated to be dense thorny scrub, but at present the vegetation is a mixture of Fynbos (healthy, fine-leafed shrubs which withstand drought conditions effectively) and a little grass, with quantities of rush (*Restionaceae*). The Strandveld, according to this classification, is found on low-lying sandy, coastal plains, with a winter rainfall of 50 to 300 mm a year. It is an open scrub vegetation, and if rested from grazing, grasses become plentiful.

To the springtime visitor to Darling and environs, certain fields are a breath-taking blaze of colour. This is not necessarily the spectacle that met the eyes of early travellers. Due to heavy grazing or bush-slashing the climax scrub vegetation has been retarded, allowing the wealth of colourful smaller bulbs and annuals to sport their full glory. Should a particular area be fenced and totally protected from grazing and burning, the vegetation would become a far less spectacular restio-scrub combination.

The Effect of Grazing and Veld Management on the Natural Flora

OBSERVATIONS BY WILFERD DUCKITT, OUDEPOST, DARLING

Our late father made regular and persistent appeals for farmers to set aside and fence off a piece of their best "flower veld" so that our beautiful floral heritage would be preserved for generations to come. This has borne fruit as many visitors know who come back again and again to drive through and enjoy these carpets of flowers in springtime. In making these appeals he always stressed the fact that these pieces of veld were not lost to the farmer but of great value to him in the way of grazing for his sheep and cattle. But at certain crucial periods all animals must be taken from these camps.

There are two kinds of veld in this west coast area of ours. Firstly, the usually wet and marshy pieces in between the grainlands, and, secondly, the sandy veld up the west coast, which is almost exclusively used for grazing. The flower camps in the grain areas can be grazed for a while after the first rains have fallen and the edible bushes have sprouted. When the young flower plants start rising off the ground and become edible, usually about the middle of June, then animals are removed from these camps so that the flowers can grow and bloom, to be enjoyed by admiring flower lovers and set seed again.

Once this has happened, sheep and cattle can once more be allowed in to enjoy late spring grasses before they get dry and unpalatable. The tiny feet of the sheep seem to have a very good effect on the germination of the flower seed. This no doubt is because the seeds are trodden into the ground and the soil well compacted. The animals eat the bigger natural bush, thus preventing the normally smaller wild flowers from being smothered or blooming unseen.

On the sandy coastal farms the camps are usually bigger, and it is more difficult to keep animals out for long periods. Rotational grazing should be practised, and it has been found a very sound practice to spare each camp for the entire growing season, once in four years, so that all flowers can set seed properly. Many of our prettiest flowers are also the most tasty, so the only way to per-petuate them is to allow a complete rest, as mentioned above.

Here judicious veld burning also seems to have beneficial effects. This can only be done during the late summer when the camp is going to be spared for the full growth period. What more beautiful sight could you wish for than a burn covered with the carpets of bright-coloured flowers which we so enjoy in springtime? Where there is dense growth of bush, burning once in about seven years is very beneficial. It opens up the veld and the flowers can breathe again. Several species are known only to flower after burning. Old unpalatable bush and reed is removed and the young shoots are once more enjoyed by animals.

Other methods of veld clearing such as dragging with a heavy girder or bush-cutting, which is very expensive, still do not seem to have so many beneficial effects as judicious burning. This is a contentious matter, but as a keen conservationist I think I have the right to say that in the Darling district burning can be carried out safely. The accent is on small burns made in late autumn when the wind has dropped, resulting in bare patches surrounded by bush to prevent wind erosion from taking place.

Further north, in the Hopefield district, where the rainfall is lower and veld recovery thus slower, burning has been banned. This is the only effective measure against fire bugs who throw a match into the veld when the summer is at its hottest and the South Easter blowing hard. The result is miles of veld burnt through probably a few farms, leaving long bare tracts for the wind to start its process of wind erosion and all the evils that follow in its wake.

Three generations of flower-loving farmers have shown that if these basic principles of veld management are followed, always varied according to local conditions and the rainfall, the future generations will be assured of enjoying the flowers which we have had the privilege of conserving and increasing, as well as being able to utilize this same veld for meat and wool.

May the ideals of our forefathers be perpetuated in the generations to come, assisted and encouraged by the authorities who fully realize the enormous benefits of conserving our natural heritage.

PLATE 1

TYPHACEAE

A temperate and tropical family of only 1 genus and 10 species. All marsh plants. The lower portion of the stem is a rhizome (creeping underground structure).

1 **Typha latifolia** *L.* ssp. **capensis** *Rohrb.*
Derivation: Typhe (Greek), a plant used for stuffing bolsters and beds; folium (Latin), leaf; capensis (Latin), from the Cape.
Common Name: Bulrush, Papkuil.
Distribution: Widespread throughout South Africa.
The inflorescence is a dense spike with male flowers on the upper portion (yellow in colour when the pollen is ripe) and browner female flowers lower down. Found only on stream banks or marshy places. Flowers December–March.

2 **Zantedeschia aethiopica** *(L.) Spreng.*
Derivation: Name honours F. Zantedeschi, born in 1797, who later became professor of physics in Padua; aethiopia (Latin), meaning Africa, but usually referring to Southern Africa.
Common Name: Varkblom.
Distribution: Widespread in the Cape.
Extremely common in marshy areas in the south western Cape. Flowers in spring.

APONOGETONACEAE

A family found in tropical areas as well as in the Republic of South Africa. There is only 1 genus with 30 species; all water plants, usually with floating basal leaves.

3 **Aponogeton angustifolius** *Ait.*
Derivation: A partial anagram of *Potamogeton*, which in turn comes from potamos (Greek), a river, and geiton (Greek), a neighbour; angustus (Latin), narrow; folium (Latin), leaf.
Distribution: Confined to the south western Cape.
The scentless flowers are arranged in forked spikes. Each flower has two perianth segments. Flowers in spring.

4 **Aponogeton distachos** *L.f.*
Derivation: Di- (Greek), two; stachys (Greek), relating to a spike.
Common Name: Wateruintjie or Waterblommetjie.
Distribution: Common in the winter rainfall areas of the Cape Province, eastwards to Plettenberg Bay.
Both the tubers and flowers are edible; the old flowers are boiled with *Oxalis* flowers, onions and mutton to make the popular waterblommetjie bredie. As in the former species, the flowers are arranged in two rows, but each has only one perianth segment. Flowers fragrant, appearing in spring.

JUNCAGINACEAE

A small cosmopolitan family (temperate and antarctic regions), frequent in salty and fresh-water marshes. Common in Australia. Three genera and 25 species.

5 **Triglochin bulbosa** *L.*
Derivation: Treis (Greek), three; glochin (Greek), a point; bulbosa (Latin), bulbous, referring to the basal parts.
Distribution: Found all over Africa, particularly in coastal salty marshes.
The leaves are broad at the base and rush-like above. The flowers are small with reduced perianth segments and prominent stigmas. Only female flowers illustrated. Flowers July–October.

1.

2.

3.

4.

5.

H. mason.

PLATE 2

GRAMINAE

One of the largest families of flowering plants, 620 genera and about 10 000 species. Found wherever plants can survive. Grasses have fibrous roots. Leaves are characteristic in having an ensheathing base and a ligule at the junction of the blade and sheath. The inflorescences are compound and made up of small flowers arranged in a series of spikelets.

1 **Spartina capensis** *Nees*

Derivation: Spartine (Greek), a cord, referring to the tough leaves; capensis (Latin), from the Cape.
Distribution: Of the 16 species (mostly American), all are salt-loving halophytes. In the Republic found all along the Cape coast, especially Algoa Bay, but seldom recorded from the western coast. The leaves are coarse, rough and in-rolled. Flowers December–January.

2 **Sporobolus virginicus** *(L.) Kunth*

Derivation: Sporos (Greek), a seed; -bolos (Greek), a throw; virginicus (Latin), from Virginia. Erroneously thought by Linnaeus to come from Virginia.
Distribution: Common in patches near the sea along Cape Coast.
A halophyte (salt-loving plant). Creeping stem with erect branches 30 cm. Spikelets crowded 2 mm long. Flowers October–March.

CYPERACEAE The sedges.

There are 90 genera and about 4 000 species in this family found all over the world. Grass-like perennials growing in wet places, but differing from grasses in that there is no articulation between leaf sheath and blade.

3 **Scirpus nodosus** *Rottb.*

Derivation: Scirpus (Latin), a rush; nodosus (Latin), knotted, knobby.
Distribution: Frequent throughout the Republic in sandy spots near the sea-shore.
The flowers are arranged in spikes and the bracts in these spikes are spirally arranged. A tufted perennial with a branched rhizome. Flowers December–March.

4 **Ficinia lateralis** *(Vahl) Kunth*

Derivation: Name in honour of D. H. Ficini, the author of a Flora of Dresden; lateralis (Latin), lateral.
Distribution: Coastal areas, south western to south eastern Cape.
Usually about 12 cm high, can be taller. A tough colonizer which tolerates salt spray and summer drought, often found in loose sand. Branches at the base to form dense spreading clumps. Flowers February–March.

JUNCACEAE

Nine genera with 400 species in temperate, arctic and tropical regions, especially in damp, cold places. The inflorescence is a rounded mass of flowers.

5 **Juncus acutus** *L.*

Derivation: Jungere (Latin), to join (flowers in clusters); acutus (Latin), acute, pointed.
Distribution: Coastal areas, west and south, as well as interior.
Leaves are sharply pointed and the flowers are in dense clusters. Flowers in September.

RESTIONACEAE

Twenty-eight genera and 320 species, mostly South African and Australian, with a few from Central Africa, Vietnam, New Zealand and Chile. Xerophytes often tufted. Flowers dioecious (males and females on separate plants).

6 **Chondropetalum tectorum** *(L.f.) Pillans*

Derivation: Chondroideus (Latin), hard and tough-like cartilage; petalum (Latin), petal; tectorum (Latin), of roofs.
Common Name: Thatching reed, Dakriet, Olifantsriet.
Distribution: South western Cape.
The most common thatching reed in the south western Cape. Stems up to 1 m tall. Spathes or basal inflorescence bracts deciduous. Flowers April–June.

7 **Chondropetalum microcarpum** *(Kunth) Pillans*

Derivation: Mikros (Latin), small; carpos (Greek), fruit.
Distribution: South western Cape to Port Elizabeth. On sandy flats.
Spreading by underground branching rhizomes. Sheaths papery and persisting during the flowering season. Flowers April—May.

8 **Willdenowia striata** *Thunb.*

Derivation: Named in honour of Karl Ludwig Willdenow, professor of botany, Berlin, 1765–1812; stria (Latin), a groove or furrow.
Common Name: Sonkwasriet.
Distribution: South western to southern Cape and western Cape to Namaqualand.
Robust tufts with branching, minutely grooved stems, up to 1 m tall. Grows especially on sandy flats, very beautiful when tan bracts reflect the sunlight. Flowers in April.

1.

2

3

4

5

6

7

8

H Mason

PLATE 3 RESTIONACEAE

1 **Chondropetalum macrocarpum** (*Kunth*) *Pillans* (female).
Derivation: Macros (Greek), large; carpos (Greek), relating to the fruit.
Distribution: Western area of south western Cape. Sandy flats and stony slopes.
Plants about 1 m tall, the female conspicuous in fruit. Unlike any other *Chondropetalum*.
Flowers in May.

2 **Thamnochortus spicigerus** *R. Br.,* (male).
Derivation: Thamnos (Greek), a shrub; chortos (Greek), green herbage; spicigera, spike bearing.
Distribution: South western to south eastern Cape, mostly on sandy flats.
Plant 1–2 m tall, forming dense tufts. Used for thatching. Flowers June–August.

3 **Thamnochortus spicigerus** (*Thunb.*) *R. Br.,* (female).

4 **Chondropetalum nudum** (*Steud.*) *Rottb.*
Derivation: Nudus (Latin), naked, i.e. devoid of leaves.
Distribution: South western Cape, in peaty-sandy soil, tolerating wet conditions in winter.
An inconspicuous plant, except where growing densely. Flowers rather similar to *C. tectorum*, but plants much shorter and slenderer. Flowers April–May.

5 **Leptocarpus vimineus** (*Rottb.*) *Pillans*
Derivation: Leptos (Greek), slender; carpos (Greek), fruit; vimineus (Latin), having long flexible shoots.
Distribution: South western Cape, in clay soil, sand or gravel, on flats and lower slopes; easily overlooked. Flowers December–February.

6 **Leptocarpus impolitus** (*Kunth*) *Pillans* (male and female).
Derivation: Impolitus (Latin), unpolished.
Distribution: Tigerberg flats to Clanwilliam coast, in sand.
Stems coarsely tubercled, slender, but eventually forming bushy plants up to 0,5 m tall.
Flowers in June.

Restio clumps — thatching reed

Plate 4 LILIACEAE

A large family of 250 genera and 3 700 species, worldwide in distribution. A few are trees and many xerophytes, but the majority are herbs. Floral parts arranged in multiples of three; ovary superior. Some economically valuable plants, *Allium* (onion) being one.

1 **Lachenalia aloides** (*L. f.*) *Hort.* var. **quadricolor** (= *L. tricolor* Jacq.).
Derivation: Named in honour of Werner von Lachenal, a professor of botany at Basel University, Switzerland; aloides (Greek), like an *Aloe*; quadricolor (Latin), four coloured.
Common Name: Klipkalossie, Vierkleurkalossie, Vierkleurtjie, Cape Cowslip.
Distribution: Malmesbury district, on rocky outcrops.
The pendulous flowers are the most colourful in the genus and bulbs have been cultivated as pot and garden plants for very many years. The species occurs naturally in a number of colour forms. It can be distinguished from the other large tubular-flowered species as the outer segments are much shorter than the inner segments. Flowers July–August.

2 **Lachenalia rubida** *Jacq.*
Derivation: Rubidus (Latin), reddish.
Common Name: Sandklossie, Rooivoëltjie.
Distribution: South western Cape, in coastal areas in sand.
It is the first species to flower and the flowers appear before the leaves are fully developed. They can be distinguished from those of *L. bulbifera* as the two upper inner segments protrude slightly beyond the lowest. Flowers April–May.

3 **Lachenalia bulbifera** (*Cyrillo*) *Hort.*
Derivation: Bulbus (Latin), bulb; fer (Latin), carrying.
Common Name: Rooinaeltjie.
Distribution: Clanwilliam to George, in sandy coastal areas.
An early flowering species with a large white, fleshy bulb. It is easily cultivated and has been grown as a pot and garden plant for many years. The outer segments are usually vermilion and only slightly shorter than the inner which are tipped with purple, often with a green central zone. Flowers May–July.

4 & 5 **Lachenalia viridiflora** *Barker*
Derivation: Viridis (Latin), green; flos (Latin), flower.
Distribution: Malmesbury and Vredenburg districts, growing on rocky outcrops.
This plant is a fairly recent discovery and has only recently been described and named. Its metallic green flowers are slightly spreading to erect and the leaves may be spotted or plain. Flowers May–June.

6 **Lachenalia reflexa** *Thunb.*
Derivation: Reflexus (Latin), turned back – referring to the recurved leaves.
Distribution: Cape Peninsula–Malmesbury, usually found in dampish places.
Easily recognised by its yellow, erect flowers in which the segments are much the same length and overlap to form a narrow mouth. The recurved leaves often have undulate or crimped edges. Flowers June–July.

7 **Lachenalia mutabilis** *Sweet*
Derivation: Mutabilis (Latin), variable, apparently referring to the tip of the inflorescence where the flowers are very much reduced or mutilated.
Distribution: Malmesbury–Namaqualand, usually found on rocky hillsides.
Leaf usually solitary with a long blade with undulate margins. The flowers are small and face downwards at an angle; blue to magenta at the base and the sterile tip of the inflorescence is the same colour. Flowers July–September.

8 **Lachenalia mediana** *Jacq.*
Derivation: Medianus (Latin), middle, intermediate.
Distribution: Malmesbury, in sandy soil, often near the sea.
Leaves broad, one or two. Plants often quite tall, up to 30 cm high, with many small flowers of opalescent colours. Flowers August–September.

PLATE 5 LILIACEAE

1 **Veltheima glauca** *Jacq.*
Derivation: Named after Frederick Augustus Veltheim, a German amateur botanist; glaucus (Latin), a grey-green colour.
Distribution: Saldanha Bay, Hopefield, Malmesbury–southern Namaqualand.
Leaves glaucous (grey-green) and narrower than in the other species. Perianth colours can vary from yellow to bright red and spotted. Flowers in September.

2 **Lachenalia unifolia** *Jacq.*
Derivation: Uni- (Latin), one; folium (Latin), leaf.
Distribution: Cape Peninsula up west coast to Clanwilliam.
Only one leaf; the free part narrow and channelled; up to 36 cm long; the clasping leaf base with distinct purple bands. Flowers are opalescent blue at the base, the inner segments whitish longer and only slightly spreading at the tips. Flowers August–September.

3 **Lachenalia hirta** *Thunb.*
Derivation: Hirtus (Latin), hairy.
Distribution: Western coastal belt from Malmesbury to Namaqualand, in sandy soil.
A dainty species with flowers blue at the base, inner segments pale yellow. Leaf solitary; the blade linear, widening at the base, with undulate margins; the whole covered with spreading bristly hairs, the clasping base banded with purple. Flowers August–September.

4 **Lachenalia contaminata** *Ait.*
Derivation: Contaminatus (Latin), unclean, probably referring to the dark patches on the petals.
Distribution: South western Cape from Bredasdorp to Piketberg, in damp areas.
Leaves six to ten, narrow and channelled, erect. Flowers with short stalks and spreading white segments, each with a dark spot at the tip. Flowers September–October.

5 **Lachenalia purpureo-coerulea** *Jacq.*
Derivation: Purpureus (Latin), purple; coeruleus (Latin), blue.
Distribution: Malmesbury district, in sandy soil.
Leaves (two) broad and flat with many raised pustules on the upper side. Flowers blue at the base, purple at the tips of the segments which are spreading; the stamens well exerted from the flowers. Flowers in October.

2

3

1.

4

5

PLATE 6 LILIACEAE

1 & 2 **Ornithogalum thyrsoides** *Jacq.*
Derivation: Ornis (Greek), a bird; gala (Greek), milk; thyrsoides (Greek), like a thyrsus; thyrsus (Latin), a flower spike in the form of an ovate panicle.
Common Name: Chinkerichee, "Tjienk".
Distribution: From Langebaan along Cape coastal areas to Grahamstown and Somerset East. The perianth segments are free, or nearly so; the three inner segments widening abruptly at the base. No. 1 is from the population on the Mamre farm, Bokbaai – these are the largest known. Flowers October–December.

3 **Ornithogalum suaveolens** *Jacq.*
Derivation: Suaveolens (Latin), fragrant, sweet-smelling.
Distribution: Found in the Sandveld, extending to southern Namaqualand.
This plant was introduced into cultivation in Europe nearly 200 years ago. The yellow perianth segments are united at the base. Three to six leaves, linear, 30 cm long. Usually flowers in October.

4 **Ornithogalum maculatum** *Jacq.*
Derivation: Maculatus (Latin), spotted or blotched.
Distribution: Malmesbury to Ceres, Calvinia and Vanrhynsdorp.
The style is very short and the filaments are much longer than they are broad. The golden-yellow or orange perianth segments have the outer segments blotched with black or brown. Flowers in spring.

5 **Bulbinella sp.**
Derivation: Bulbinella (Latin), a little bulbus plant.
Distribution: Kalabaskraal.
This genus is in need of revision. Flowers in April.

1

4

2

3

5

HALF SIZE

H mason.

PLATE 7 LILIACEAE

1 **Eucomis nana** *Ait.*
Derivation: Eucomes (Greek), beautiful headed, referring to the crown of leaves; nanus (Greek), dwarf.
Distribution: Widespread.
About eight flattened leaves. The inflorescence stalk is club-shaped and purple spotted. Perianth segments green. Flowers in October.

2 **Kniphofia uvaria** *(L.) Hook.*
Derivation: The genus honours Johannes Hieronymus Kniphof (1704–'63), professor of medicine at Erfurt, Germany.
Common Name: Vuurpyl, redhot poker.
Distribution: Widespread in the Cape.
Leaves keeled or V-shaped in section. Flowers December – June.

Meeuwklip - Langebaan

2

1.

H.mason

PLATE 8 LILIACEAE

1 **Drimia elata** *Jacq.*
Derivation: Drimus (Greek), pungent – referring to the bulbs which are used as an emetic; Elatus (Latin), tall.
Common Name: Jeukbol (leaves and flowers produce skin irritant); Jeukrui.
Distribution: Widespread in the Cape.
Bulbs very large with reddish-purple flesh. Flower stalks up to 1 m. Perianth segments all equal, greenish-brown, often reflexed; filaments widened at base. Flowers February–March.

2 **Bulbinella triquetra** *Kunth*
Derivation: Bulbinella (Latin), a little bulbous plant; triquetrus (Latin), three cornered, triangular.
Common Name: Geel Katstert.
Distribution: South western Cape coastal region and Namaqualand.
Underground portions not a bulb. Stamens not bearded. Leaves threadlike. Flowers August–October.

3 **Hyacinthus paucifolius** *Barker*
Derivation: Greek mythological hero, Hyacinthus. On his death, Apollo changed his blood into the flower that bears his name; paucifolius (Latin), few-leaved.
Distribution: Cape Province, especially damp sandy soil near the sea.
Perianth segments pink, all alike, bracts not spurred. Stamens attached to the perianth. Flowers in autumn.

4 **Dipidax triquetra** *Baker*
Derivation: Di- (Greek), two; pidax (Greek), a spring; triquetrus (Latin), triangular.
Common Name: Waterblom.
Distribution: Cape flats to Clanwilliam.
Stem with three leaves. Perianth segments free; three styles as long as the ovary which is three-angled. Flowers sessile. Grows in water. Flowers August–September.

5 **Dipidax punctata** *(L.) Hutch.*
Derivation: Punctus (Latin), spotted.
Distribution: Clanwilliam to Swellendam.
Leaves ovate to lanceolate and not three-angled like former. Grows on moist gravelly slopes. Flowers August–September.

6 **Bulbine annua** *Willd.*
Derivation: Bulbine (Latin), a bulbous plant; annus (Latin), annual.
Distribution: South western Cape. Perennial with a tuberous or woody rootstock. Leaves fleshy and fully developed at flowering time. Stamens bearded. Flowers September–October.

7 **Bulbine favosa** *Roem. & Schult.*
Derivation: Favosus (Latin), honey-combed.
Distribution South western Cape in sandy areas.
Height 15–30 cm. Rootstock fleshy. Two to three leaves 3 mm in diameter appear after the flowers. Flowers have strong sweet perfume. Stamens bearded. The seeds are rough, sharp and angled. Flowers March–July.

8 **Tulbaghia capensis** *Jacq.*
Derivation: Named in honour of Ryk Tulbagh, an early Cape Governor; capensis (Latin), of the Cape.
Common Name: Garlic.
Distribution: South western Cape to Namaqualand.
The flower head is an umbel. The flowers each have a special petaloid outgrowth, a corona. In this species the flowers are always shades of yellow through dull green to brown. Flowers in spring.

1.

2.

3.

4.

5.

6.

7.

8.

H. mason.

PLATE 9 LILIACEAE

1 **Asparagus crispus** *Lam.*
Derivation: Crispus (Latin), waved; twisted, crisped.
Distribution: St. Helena Bay to Swellendam and inland to Worcester.
Cladodes not flattened. Stems annual, weak and climbing; much branched and zig-zagging at the nodes. Flowers June–October.

2 **Asparagus asparagoides** *(L.) Wight*
Derivation: Asparagoides (Greek), like an asparagus.
Distribution: Widespread throughout South Africa.
Cladodes flattened with more than one vein. Stems smooth and climbing. Flowers June–September.

3 **Ornithoglossum viride** *(L.f.) Ait.*
Derivation: Ornis (Greek), a bird; glossa (Greek), a tongue; viridis (Latin), green.
Distribution: South western Cape.
The individual flowers are stalked. The perianth segments are free and at the base of each segment there are nectaries. Flowers June–September.

4 **Urginea exuviata** *Steinh.*
Derivation: Derived from Beni Urgin, a place in Algeria where the first described plant in this genus was found; exuviae (Latin), that which is cast aside, i.e. a skin; an allusion to its tendency to shed the dry bulb scales.
Distribution: Cape Peninsula to Vanrhynsdorp.
Leaves and flowers appear together, most commonly after fires. The scales clasp the bulb and inner ones are prolonged into a loose sheath with transverse bars. Flowers very fragrant. Flowers in September–October.

5 **Urginea filifolia** *(Jacq.) Steinh.*
Derivation: Filum (Latin), thread; folium (Latin), leaf.
Distribution: Bredasdorp to Vanrhynsdorp and inland to Worcester and Ceres.
The scales do not clasp the bulb but the inner one is prolonged to form a purple ribbed sheath. Three to nine (usually six) leaves; wiry and green appearing at the same time as the flowers. The outside of the perianth segments is red-purple to brown. Flowers August–September.

1.

2.

3.

4.

5.

H Mason

PLATE 10 LILIACEAE

1 **Chlorophytum triflorum** (*Ait.*) *Kunth*
Derivation: Chloros (Greek), green; phyton (Greek), a plant; triflorus (Latin), three flowered.
Distribution: Cape Peninsula to Clanwilliam.
Flower stalks have a joint in them. Perianth persistent. Flowers remain open all day. Leaves in this species not flat but folded. Flowers October–November.

2 **Albuca canadensis** (*L.*) *Leighton*
Derivation: Albus (Latin), white; canadensis (Latin), from Canada: it was mistaken for a Canadian plant when named.
Common Name: Slangtamarak, Koppie-en-Piering, Lanternblom.
Distribution: Widespread.
The peduncle is edible. Flowers in September.

3 **Asparagus thunbergianus** *Schult.*
Derivation: Aspharagos (Greek), the name given to edible Asparagus; thunbergianus: named in honour of Carl Pehr Thunberg, a Swedish botanist who visited the Cape in 1772–1775 and wrote an excellent account of his travels.
Common Name: Kartdoring, Kat-en-Doringbos.
Distribution: Clanwilliam, Malmesbury, Cape Peninsula to Uitenhage.
Spines are formed from modified leaves. Not a climber, stems erect and straight; branches brown. Flowers March–June.

4 **Asparagus aethiopicus** *L.* var. **aethiopicus**
Derivation: Aethiopicus (Latin), belonging to Africa.
Distribution: Confined to the Cape Province – usually coastal forests.
Cladodes flattened and one veined, several at one node. Branches grooved. Flowers January–October.

5 **Trachyandra revoluta** (*L.*) *Kunth*
Derivation: Trachys (Greek), rough; andro (Greek), male; revolutus (Latin), rolled back.
This genus which was separated from *Anthericum* usually has rough filaments.
Distribution: Eastern to western Cape near coast.
A stout plant found on completely loose dune sand. The lower half of the filaments are rough. Flowers have a heavy musk-like odour. They flower freely after fires and the flowers only open in the late afternoon. Flowers August–November.

6 **Wurmbea spicata** (*Burm.*) *Dur. & Schinz*
Derivation: Named in honour of F. von Wurmb, a Dutch merchant; spicatus (Latin), bearing a spike.
Common Name: Kaffertjie.
Distribution: Widespread all over the Cape Province.
The perianth segments minutely united at the base. Flowers September–October.

1.

2

3

4

5   H Mason

6

PLATE 11 LILIACEAE

1 Massonia sp.

An as yet undescribed species collected on the Donkergat peninsula. The filaments are white and the anthers are black. Flowers in May.

2 Massonia nervosa *Hornem.*

Derivation: Named in honour of Francis Masson, a gardener sent out from Kew in 1772 to collect at the Cape; nervosus (Latin), nerved or veined.
Distribution: Only known from the Saldanha Bay area.
The flowers have minute bracts. The perianth tube is long and bluish and there is usually a conspicuous drop of nectar in the throat of the tube. Flowers in June.

3 Massonia obovata *Jacq.*

Derivation: Obovate describes the leaf shape.
Distribution: Western Cape coastal area.
The flowers have a shorter tube than nervosa and a very distinct and large bract. Flowers in spring.

4 Aloe distans *Haw.*

Derivation: Aloe (Greek), aloe; distans (Latin), standing apart.
Distribution: Along a narrow coastal strip near Saldanha Bay.
The plants are often prostrate with leaves on the turned-up terminal parts only. The leaf margins have a white cartilaginous edge with blunt teeth. The plant appears to be confined to limestone ridges. Flowers December–March.

Aloe distans

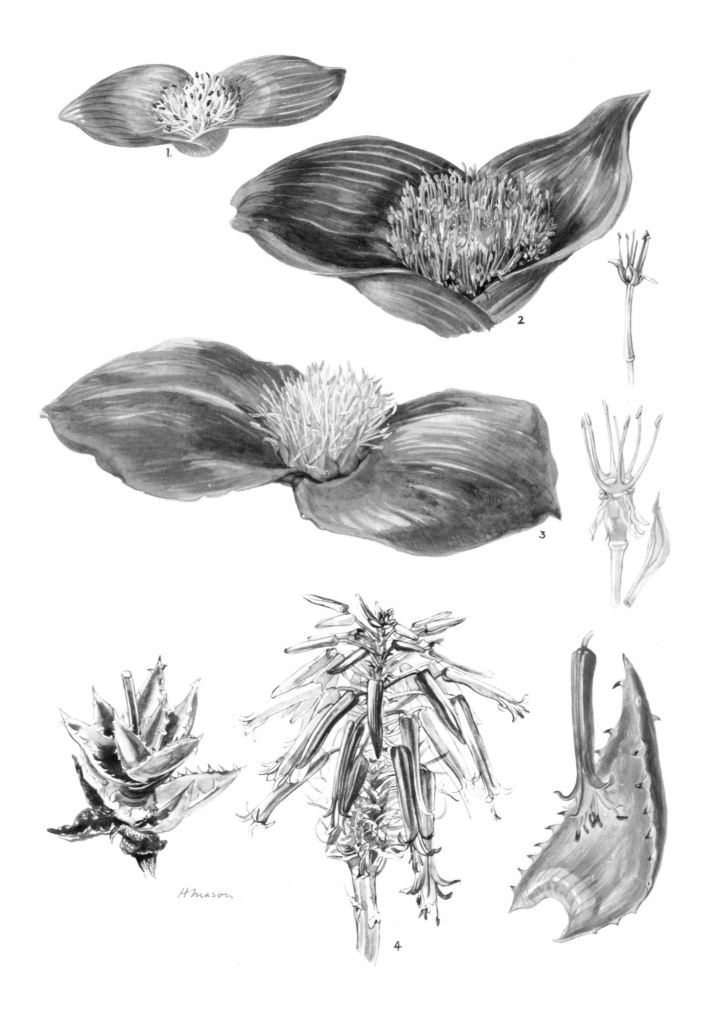

1.

2

3

4

H mason

PLATE 12 HAEMODORACEAE

There are 14 genera and 75 species – mainly South African, Australian and tropical American. Flowers have three or six stamens and these often show a dimorphism with the style.

1 Wachendorfia paniculata L.

Derivation: Named in honour of E. J. von Wachendorff, professor of botany and chemistry at Utrecht (1702–1758); paniculata (Latin), like a panicle which is a type of arrangement of flowers in a head.

Common Name: Rooikanol, Koffiepit.

Distribution: Widespread along the Cape coastal area.

The leaves are pleated, and the rootstock is always red or orange in colour. Perianth segments are broad (up to 1,6 cm) and the stamens are nearly as long as the perianth. The three upper perianth segments are joined at the base. These flowers show an interesting dimorphic arrangement – two stamens point to the left and a single stamen and style to the right. This arrangement is consistent in one plant whereas in another plant the opposite is the case, with two stamens to the right and the single stamen and style to the left. It is thought that only pollen from a right-handed stamen polinates a left-handed stigma. Flowers August–December.

2 & 3 Cyanella hyacinthoides L.

Derivation: Cuanos (Greek), blue; hyacinthoides (Greek), hyacinth-like.

Distribution: Cape Peninsula and south western Cape.

This is an endemic genus, and it differs from the other members of the family in having six stamens. There is still uncertainty about the exact relationships between the genera of this family. Research is being conducted at the moment particularly with regard to the dimorphic nature of the stamens. (Expl. under *Wachendorfia.*) Perianth from white, pink to mauve. Flowers October–April.

4 Cyanella lutea L. f.

Derivation: Luteus (Latin), deep yellow.

Distribution: Widespread in the Cape Province.

Perianth segments longer than former species. A pink form is known in eastern Cape. Flowers in October.

46

1.

2

3

4

Wilson

PLATE 13 HYPOXIDACEAE

Seven genera and 120 species. World-wide except in Europe and northern Asia. Plants have a tuberous rhizome or corm. The ovary is inferior.

1 **Spiloxene capensis** (*L.*) *Garside*
Derivation: Spilos (Greek), spot; xenos (Greek), host; capensis (Latin), of the Cape.
Common Name: Peacock flower, Sterretjie, Poublommetjie.
Distribution: Widespread in the south western Cape.
Corms fibrous; leaves V-shaped in cross section; bracts large, leaf-like; flowers white or yellow (occasionally pale pink) with or without an iridescent or dark spot at the base of the perianth segments. Flowers August–September.

2 **Spiloxene canaliculata** *Garside*
See Plate 14: 1.

3 **Spiloxene alba** (*Thunb.*) *Fourcade*
Derivation: Albus (Latin), white.
Common Name: Witsterretjie.
Distribution: Cape Peninsula, Swellendam, Ceres, Stellenbosch.
Corm fleshy with very loose fibrous scales; leaves round in cross section; bracts two, leaf-like; flowers white with maroon reverse; ovary constricted to form a neck. Flowers April–May.

4 **Spiloxene schlechteri** (*Bol.*) *Garside*
Derivation: Named after Rudolph Schlechter, a late nineteenth century plant collector.
Common Name: Sterretjie.
Distribution: Cape Peninsula, Stellenbosch, Caledon, Clanwilliam.
Corm surrounded by unbranched curved black spines outside the netted scales; leaves terete; flowers yellow, reddish brown on the reverse. Flowers June–September.

5 **Spiloxene serrata** (*Thunb.*) *Garside*
Derivation: Serra (Latin), saw.
Common Name: Gouesterretjie.
Distribution: Widespread in the south western Cape.
Corm covered with netted and twisted roots; leaves grass-like with small teeth on the margins; bracts two, hairlike; flowers yellow (occasionally white). Flowers June–September.

Empodium veratrifolium in rock crevices

1

5

2

3

4

henson

PLATE 14 HYPOXIDACEAE

1 **Spiloxene canaliculata** *Garside*
Derivation: Spilos (Greek), a spot; xenos (Greek), a host; canaliculatus (Latin), channelled.
Common Name: Geelsterretjie.
Distribution: Darling, Malmesbury to Cape Peninsula.
Near *S. capensis* but leaves channelled (U-shaped in cross-section). Seeds J-shaped. Flowers deep orange with a dark central spot. Flowers July–November.

2 **Spiloxene aquatica** *(L. f.) Fourcade*
Derivation: Aquaticus (Latin), growing in water.
Common Name: Watersterretjie, Vleiblommetjie.
Distribution: Cape Peninsula to Namaqualand.
Corm fleshy, almost naked; leaves round in cross-section with a spongy white pith. Flowers – two to seven, arranged in umbels. Flowers June–October.

3 **Spiloxene ovata** *(L. f.) Garside*
Derivation: Ovatus (Latin), ovate (shape of leaf).
Common Name: Geelsterretjie.
Distribution: Widespread in the south western Cape.
Leaves the broadest in the genus, somewhat fleshy; bract small thread-like; flowers yellow – often reddish on the reverse. Flowers August–October.

4 **Pauridia minuta** *(L. f.) Dur. & Schinz*
Derivation: Pauridios (Greek), very small; minutus (Latin), very small.
Common Name: Koringsterretjie.
Distribution: Widespread in the south western Cape.
Perianth tube short; two small hairlike bracts about halfway down the flower stalk; leaves vary from flat and broad to linear. Flowers April–June.

5 **Pauridia longituba** *Thompson*
Derivation: Longus (Latin), long; tubus (Latin), tube, referring to the long perianth tube.
Distribution: Vredenburg. Known only in shallow soil on granite outcrops in this district.
Similar to *P. minuta* but with a very long perianth tube. The bracts are adjacent to the base of the ovary. Flowers in June.

6 **Empodium veratrifolium** *(Willd.) Thompson*
Derivation: Empodios (Greek), at one's feet; in the way; veratrum (Latin), hellebore, i.e. leaves like *Veratrum*, the hellebore; folium (Latin), leaf.
Distribution: Saldanha Bay area.
Differs from *Empodium plicatum* because the flowers and leaves appear at the same time. There is a very short beak to the ovary which is not enclosed in the sheathing leaves. Flowers in June.

7 **Empodium plicatum** *(L. f.) Salisb.*
Derivation: Plicatus (Latin), folded into pleats lengthwise.
Common Name: Autumn Star; Ploegtydblommetjie.
Distribution: Western and southern Cape.
The ovary is produced into a long neck resembling the flower stalk. The ovary and fruit remain hidden in the leaf bases. Flowers April–June.

1.

2.

3.

4.

5.

6.

7.

7.

4.

H Mason

PLATE 15 AMARYLLIDACEAE

Eighty-five genera, 1 100 species. Mainly tropical or sub-tropical. Plants usually with large bulbs. Inflorescence often umbel-like. Six stamens in two whorls with an inferior ovary. Many popular garden plants like the Narcissus and Daffodil belong to this family.

1 **Boophone guttata** *Herb.*

Derivation: Bous (Greek), an ox; phonos (Greek), slaughter, alluding to the poisonous properties of the bulb; gutta (Latin), a drop of fluid; guttatus – spotted.
Common Name: Suuroogblom.
Distribution: South western Cape.
Perianth tube is short. Two large bracts below the heads of flowers. Flowers rarely, except after fires. Flowers March–April; leaves in May. The bulb is extremely toxic.

2 **Cybistetes longifolia** (*L.*) *Milne Red. & Schw.*

Derivation: Kubisteter (Greek), a tumbler (ref. to the mature inflorescence rolling round by the wind); longifolius (Latin), long-leafed.
Common Name: Malagas Lily.
Distribution: Widespread in the Cape Province.
Perianth tube very short with free segments longer than 2 cm. The flowers are more or less regular and the ovary is not conspicuously angled. Strongly fragrant. Leaves continue growing from base perennially although upper portion does die down annually. Flowers February–April.

Ondervloer, Langebaan

2

times ½

1.

1.

+5

30 centimeters long.

H. Mason.

PLATE 16 AMARYLLIDACEAE

1 **Amaryllis belladonna** *L.*
Derivation: Amaryllis – a countrywoman mentioned by Virgil; belladonna – beautiful lady.
Common Name: Belladonna or March lily.
Distribution: South western Cape.

Flowers heavily scented. Perianth segments are well joined at the base; pale pink colour deepens as flowers age. Flowers exceptionally well after fire. Cultivated in England by 1700. Flowers February–April but leaves appear only in May.

2 **Gethyllis afra** *L.*
Derivation: From the Greek gethyom, a species of onion; the bulb resembles an onion; -afer (Latin), from Africa.
Common Name: Kukumakranka.
Distribution: South western Cape.

This plant is found only in the Cape (endemic). Leaves, flowers and fruit are borne separately and at different times. The fruit is borne above the ground and is fleshy, juicy and heavily scented. Eagerly sought by children. Adults in rural areas soak the fruit in brandy and use the resultant medicinal drink mainly for cure of colic. This species has white flowers with reddish markings on the reverse. The number of anthers is very variable, from six upwards. Flowers in December, leaves in July.

3 **Hessea chaplinii** *Barker*
Derivation: The genus is named to honour a German missionary at the Cape, the Rev. Hesse, who was a great friend of Burchell and other early travellers. The species' name honours a James Chaplin of the R.A.F. who collected it.
Distribution: In the Saldanha Bay area, growing near sea.

The leaves are hairy and emerge through an enclosing white sheath. Flowers March–April, leaves May–June.

4 **Hessea tenella** *(L. f.) Oberm.*
Derivation: Tenellus (Latin), delicate.
Distribution: Cape Peninsula to Tulbagh.

Peduncle straight and leaves filiform. The bulb has a membraneous tunic which is produced 2,5 cm above its neck. Stamens and styles are the same length and both are shorter than the perianth segments. Flowers March–July.

1.

2.

3.

4.

H Mason

PLATE 17 AMARYLLIDACEAE

1 **Brunsvigia orientalis** *(L.) Ait. ex Eckl.*
Derivation: Named in honour of the Duke of Brunswick; orientalis (Latin), eastern.
Common Name: Kandelaar or Candalabra flower, Misryblom.
Distribution: Widespread in the Cape.
The flowers are markedly zygomorphic – the ovary and fruits are distinctly angled. Leaves up to six spreading on the ground. The whole inflorescence breaks away when dry and the fleshy ripe seeds are shaken out as the dry inflorescence is blown around in the wind. Flowers in March and the leaves appear in May.

Lynch Point, Saldanha Bay

1.

H. Mason.

PLATE 18 AMARYLLIDACEAE

1 & 2 **Haemanthus pubescens** *L. f.*
Derivation: Haima (Greek), blood; anthos (Greek), a flower; pubescens (Latin), becoming downy.
Common Name: April fool, Skeerkwas.
Distribution: Worcester and Malmesbury, now extinct on the Cape Peninsula.
This plant has very characteristic large scaly bulbs. Leaves drying off in summer. Four or more red and showy persistent bracts ascend around the head of flowers. Flower stalk usually red. Leaves 3–4 cm broad and hairy. A small bulb covered by the papery darker outer bract is illustrated. Flowers March–April; leaves May.

3 **Haemanthus coccineus** *L.*
Derivation: Coccineus (Latin), deep red.
Common Name: April fool, Blood flower, Skeerkwas.
Distribution: Cape Peninsula to Sandveld.
Flower stalk usually green and mottled with minute purple dots. Five–ten showy red bracts. Leaves 10–20 cm broad–glabrous. Flowers March–April; leaves May.

Strip ploughing near Yserfontein

1.

1.

3

5 times.

3

2

2

H. Mason.

PLATE 19 IRIDACEAE

Sixty genera and 800 species. Tropical and temperate, chiefly in South Africa and tropical America. Flowers with only three stamens and an inferior ovary.

1 **Lapeirousia jacquinii** *N.E. Br.*
Derivation: Commemorates J. F. G. de la Peyrouse, a French naturalist of the 18th century. Specific name honours Baron N. J. von Jacquin, an 18th-century professor of chemistry and botany at Vienna.
Distribution: Widespread in the Cape.
The corm is bell-shaped. Lower leaf, not illustrated here, is very long. Perianth tube is long and slender; flowers purple, magenta or white. Flowers in September.

2 **Lapeirousia corymbosa** *(L.) Ker*
Derivation: Corymbus (Latin), with flowers in a cluster.
Distribution: Citrusdal to Bredasdorp.
The flowers are more regular than in other species, with a shorter tube. The bracts are short. This large-flowered form is confined to the Darling area. Flowers in spring.

3 **Babiana stricta** *(Ait.) Ker* var. **regia** *Lewis*
Derivation: Strictus (Latin), drawn close together, very upright; regius (Latin), regal.
Distribution: Stellenbosch, Paarl, Durbanville to Mamre.
The leaves are erect and firmly pleated. Flowers are dark blue-purple almost always with a red ring in the centre. Flowers in September.

4 **Babiana blanda** *(L. Bol.) Lewis*
Derivation: Blandus (Latin), charming; alluring.
Distribution: Melkbosstrand to Darling.
The perianth lobes are more than 1 cm broad. The filaments are barely exerted from the perianth tube. The five to six leaves are very pleated. This species hybridizes easily. Flowers August–September.

5 **Babiana pygmaea** *(Burm. f.) N. E. Br.*
Derivation: Pygmaeus (Latin), dwarf.
This strangely inappropriate name was arrived at because when named it was confused with the very small *Babiana nana*.
Distribution: Hopefield; Darling; Malmesbury.
Flowers very large – always yellow with a deep purple centre. It grows particularly in low-lying sandy areas. Flowers August–September.

6 **Hesperantha erecta** *Benth.*
Derivation: Hesperos (Greek), evening; anthos (Greek), a flower; erectus (Latin), straight up.
Distribution: Sandveld.
Three long narrow leaves. Flowers always pink with a straight tube – the style branches nearly as long as the free petals. Flowers in August.

3

6

5

1.

5

H. Mason.

2

PLATE 20 IRIDACEAE

1 Anomatheca viridis (*Ait.*) *Goldbl.*

Derivation: Anomalus (Latin), abnormal; theca (Latin), a case; viridis (Latin), green.
Distribution: Sandveld to Namaqualand.
Many leaves arranged in a fan. The corms have fibrous tunics, as in the genus *Lapeirousia* the three style-branches are forked. The capsule is distinct from other Iridaceae. Flowers in spring.

2 Lapeirousia anceps (*L.f.*) *Ker*

Derivation: Named in honour of Baron Phillipe de la Peyrouse, a French naturalist; anceps (Latin), two edged.
Distribution: Cape Peninsula to Saldanha Bay and Clanwilliam, especially on sandy flats.
Corm is typically bell-shaped with entire woody tunics. The style branches in this genus are always divided and the perianth tube is long and slender. The valves of the spathe (bracts subtending the flower) are large. Flowers in November.

3 Babiana tubulosa *Ker-gawl* var. tubiflora (*L.f.*) *Lewis*

Derivation: Generic name is an anglicized version – "Babianer" – of the Afrikaans bobbejane (baboons); the corms of the *Babiana* being a favourite food of the baboons; tubilosus (Latin), tubular; tubiflorus (Latin), with tube-shaped flowers.
Common Name: Painted Lady (used only in Darling district).
Distribution: Confined to the flats and low hills on the coast near Hopefield and Malmesbury.
Flowers cream with reddish-purple markings; with an exceptionally long tube. The style branches are not divided. Flowers September–October.

4 Babiana nana (*Andr.*) *Spreng.*

Derivation: Nanus (Latin), dwarf.
Common Name: Bobbejaantjie.
Distribution: Milnerton to Piketberg.
Leaves pubescent, lower ones oblong. Perianth tube shorter than the lobes. Flowers very fragrant, blue, mauve or pink. Flowers August–September.

5 Babiana ambigua (*Roem. & Schult.*) *Lewis*

Derivation: Ambiguus (Latin), doubtful.
Distribution: Coastal region, Riversdale to Clanwilliam.
Bracts and bracteoles usually green, rarely brown, flowers distinctly irregular. Two lateral perianth segments always with cream markings. Fragrant. Flowers September.

2

3

5

1.

4

Hmason

PLATE 21 IRIDACEAE

1 **Ixia curta** *Andr.*
Derivation: Ixia (Greek), name of a plant noted for its variability of colour; curtus (Latin), shortened.
Common Name: Kalossie.
Distribution: Sandy flats and hilly slopes – Malmesbury and Hopefield.
Flowers regular and stamens symmetric; long-tubed; bright orange flowers often with a browner-green stain in the centre. The genus *Ixia* is endemic in the Cape Province. Flowers in October.

2 **Ixia maculata** *L.*
Derivation: Maculatus (Latin), spotted; blotched.
Common Name: Geel Kalossie; Yellow Ixia.
Distribution: Although formerly much more widely spread, now confined to sandy flats and hills in the Malmesbury area.
Distinguishing characters are the large conspicuous papery bracts and bracteoles. Filaments are sometimes free but more often connate at the base. Flowers September–October.

3 **Ixia paniculata** *de la Roche*
Derivation: Paniculata describes the arrangement of the flowers.
Distribution: From Cape Peninsula to Clanwilliam.
Flower stem up to 1 m. Flowers very variable in colour and shape, but the perianth segments are consistently less than half as long as the tube. Flowers September–December.

4 **Ixia odorata** *Ker* var. **hesperanthoides** *Lewis*
Derivation: Odoratus (Latin), scented; hesperanthoides – like the genus, *Hesperantha*.
Distribution: Piketberg to Worcester.
The style branches are long but the filaments are short. The perianth tube gradually widens to become funnel-shaped before the perianth segments spread. The flowers are fragrant and the colourless papery bracts are tinged with red-brown. Flowers late September–December.

5 **Ixia scillaris** *L.*
Derivation: Scilla (Latin), a sea-leek; squill.
Common Name: Agretjie.
Distribution: From Namaqualand through to Caledon and inland on mountain slopes.
The plants in the drier interior are taller and more robust with three–four leaves. The sandveld form is smaller and more branched with four–seven leaves. In the Mamre area intermediates are found. The flowers have a short perianth tube and are zygomorphic (irregular) with pendulous asymmetric anthers. Flowers August–November.

2

H mason

5

1.

3

4

PLATE 22 IRIDACEAE

1 **Ixia conferta** *Foster* var. **ochroleuca** *(Ker) Lewis*
Derivation: Confertus (Latin), pressed close together; crowded; ochroleucus (Greek), yellowish.
Distribution: Clanwilliam to Paarl.
Bracts streaked with reddish brown. This variety differs from the species in that the flowers are yellowish with a centre that can be brown to purple (not red with purple-black centre). The stamens are long and protrude beyond the tube. Flowers September–October.

2 **Ixia capillaris** *L.f.*
Derivation: Ixos (Latin), bird-lime, referring to the clammy juice; capillaris – adjectival form of capillus (Latin), hair; hair's width; often defined as 0,18 mm.
Distribution: From Riversdale and Ladismith to the Cape Peninsula and Clanwilliam.
The perianth tube is short and only half as long as the lobes. Flowers laxly arranged on the stem. The branchlets are usually one flowered but may be two or three flowered. The bracts have three very definite dark veins. Flowers July–September.

3 **Ixia monadelpha** *de la Roche*
Derivation: Monadelphus (Latin), stamens or filaments united to form one.
Distribution: Cape Peninsula to Tulbagh.
Filaments united for at least half their length. Flower colours very variable from white to pinks and blues and even orange, with or without a deeply coloured centre. Flowers October–December.

4 **Ixia framesii** *L. Bol.*
Derivation: The species honours P. Ross Frames, C.M.G., who made a very extensive collection of Cape plants.
Distribution: The Darling district.
Perianth tube as long as the lobes. Bracts are torn at the tip – dull red-brown coloured and inconspicuously veined. Flowers September–October.

5 **Ixia odorata** *Ker*
Derivation: Odoratus (Latin), scented.
Distribution: Mainly Paarl and Stellenbosch districts but extending to Darling.
The bracts are papery and often 3-pointed with distinct brown veins. The flowers are fragrant. Flowers October–December.

5

1

H mason

2

4

3

PLATE 23 IRIDACEAE

1 **Romulea flava** (*Lam.*) *de Vos*
Derivation: Named after Romulus, founder of Rome; flavus (Latin), yellow.
Common Name: Froetang (frutang), or Knikkertjies.
Distribution: South western Cape.
All Romulea species have flowers borne singly at the ends of bare peduncles and they all share the same common name.
Flowers bright yellow, pale yellow or white. The corm has a crescent-shaped ridge at its base. Flowers June–August.

2 **Romulea flava** a white flowered form.

3 **Romulea hirsuta** *Baker*
Derivation: Hirsutus (Latin), hairy.
Distribution: South western Cape.
Leaves sometimes minutely pilose. Corm bell-shape. Flowers August–September.

4 **Romulea schlechteri** *Beguinot*
Derivation: Specific name honours Rudolf Schlechter, who between 1891–1898 collected more than 12 000 botanical specimens in South Africa.
Distribution: Near Mamre.
Flowers cream with a yellow cup. Corm as in *R. flava*. Flowers July – September.

5 **Romulea tabularis** *Beguinot*
Derivation: Tabularis (Latin), of Table Mountain, as it was thought to have come from there.
Distribution: Near Darling.
Flowers blue with a yellow cup, or rarely white. Stigmas sometimes overtopping the anthers. Corm as in *R. flava*. Flowers July–October.

6 **Romulea obscura** *Klatt* var. **campestris** *de Vos*
Derivation: Obscurus (Latin), dark, shady, indistinct; campestris (Latin), pertaining to plains or flat areas.
Distribution: Near Geelbek and southern end of Saldanha Bay.
Flowers orange-yellow, sometimes with dark blotches in the throat. Corm rounded at the base with bent basal teeth. Flowers in September.

7 **Romulea eximia** *de Vos*
Derivation: Eximius (Latin), lovely, excellent.
Distribution: Near Darling.
Flowers generally deep pink (rarely pale pink as in the figure), with dark red blotches in the throat and a greenish-yellow cup. Corm pointed at the base, with straight basal teeth. Flowers August–September.

8 **Sparaxis grandiflora** (*de la Roche*) *Ker* ssp. **fimbriata** (*Lam.*) *Goldbl.*
Derivation: Sparaxis (Greek), tearing; grandiflorus (Latin), with big flowers; fimbriatus (Latin), fringed.
Common Name: Botterblom.
Distribution: Piketberg to Faure near Cape Town.
The perianth segments broad, and cream coloured often marked with purple. Flowers in September.

9 **Hesperantha falcata** *Ker*
Derivation: Hesperos (Greek), evening; anthos (Greek), a flower; falcatus (Latin), curved like a sickle.
Common Name: Aandblommetjie.
Distribution: Calvinia to Knysna.
The leaves are glabrous, short and about 5–8 mm broad and sickle-shaped. The flowers open in the late afternoon and evening. Flowers July–October.

H mason

PLATE 24 IRIDACEAE

1 **Hexaglottis lewisiae** *Goldbl.*
(The old name *H. flexuosa* has recently been found to be illegitimate.)
Derivation: Hexa- (Greek), six; glossa (Greek), a tongue; lewisiae honours the late Dr. Joyce Lewis who for many years worked on the South African Iridaceae.
Distribution: Common in the southern and south western Cape to Namaqualand.
The corm tunics have woody spine-tipped fibres. The flowers have an unpleasant scent. Plants are up to 60 cm tall. Flowers October–November.

2 **Homeria flaccida** *Sweet*
(Treated as *Homeria breyniana* var. *aurantiaca* in "Flora of the Cape Peninsula".)
Derivation: Flaccidus (Latin), flabby, not able to hold up its own weight – referring to the petals.
Common Name: Tulp.
Distribution: Piketberg to Swellendam.
The plants have only one long leaf – the others are short sheaths. The perianth segments are broad, tapering only at the very base; three style branches flattened at the top. The flowers last only one day. Flowers September–October.

3 **Homeria collina** *Thunb.*
Derivation: Collinus (Latin), pertaining to hills.
Distribution: Widespread.
Very poisonous – it has even caused human deaths. Flowers yellow and salmon. Perianth segments not flaccid and broader than *Homeria flaccida*. Flowers July–August.

4 **Melasphaerula ramosa** *(L.) N. E. Br.*
Derivation: Melas (Greek), black; sphaerula, a latinised diminutive of sphaira – a sphere referring to the cormlets round the base of mature corm; ramosus (Latin), branched.
Common Name: Feëklokkies.
Distribution: South western Cape to Knysna.
Leaves sword-shaped. Three style branches; the perianth lobes are pointed and free almost from the base. Flowers July–September.

5 **Synnotia villosa** *(Burm. f.) N. E. Br.*
Derivation: Named in honour of W. Synnot, who collected many plants at the Cape; villosus (Latin), hairy.
Distribution: South western Cape.
Leaves glabrous and not pleated. Bracts lacerated at the top. Perianth with a short or long tube; lobes unequal and not symmetrically arranged. The specific name is misleading because the leaves are not hairy. Flowers August–September.

1.

H.Mason.   5

2

3

4

PLATE 25 IRIDACEAE

1 Ferraria framesii *L. Bol.*

Derivation: Named by Linnaeus in honour of the Italian botanist, J. B. Ferrari; the species honours P. Ross Frames, a Cape collector.

Distribution: Darling to Clanwilliam and south western Cape.

The flowers are fugitive, lasting only through the morning. Flowers have unpleasant foetid smell. Flowers in October.

2 Ferraria undulata *L.*

Derivation: Undulatus (Latin), wavy.

Common Name: Spinnekopblom; called Krulletjies in the Darling district.

Distribution: Coastal area, Piketberg to Mossel Bay.

This plant was grown in Dutch gardens in 1640 and was illustrated in a publication in 1646. It was, however, only named many years later. In Curtis's Botanical Magazine of 1790 it is referred to as "One of the most singular and beautiful of nature's productions". Flowers have unpleasant smell. Flowers August–October.

3 Ferraria antherosa *Ker*

Derivation: Antherosa (Latin), with well-developed anthers.

Common Name: Krulletjie.

Distribution: Clanwilliam, Malmesbury to Mamre.

Flowers August–October.

4 Aristea africana *(L.) Hoffmg.*

Derivation: Arista (Latin), a point – alluding to the leaves; africanus (Latin), from africa.

Common Name: Koringblommetjie.

Distribution: South western Cape coastal region.

The leaves in this species are flat and the flowers are arranged in terminal clusters. The spathes, bracts and bracteoles all have finely lacerated margins. Flowers August–December.

5 Galaxia ovata *Thunb.*

Derivation: Galaxias (Greek), the milky way. These plants are locally abundant and look like stars on the ground; ovatus (Latin), oval referring to the shape of the leaf.

Distribution: An endemic Cape genus.

Outer leaves broad. Flowers sessile with long perianth tube. Filaments united round the style. Stigma lobes fringed. Flowers July–August.

6 Galaxia fugacissima *(L. f.) Druce*

Derivation: Fugax (Latin), fleeting – the most fleeting.

Distribution: South western Cape.

The leaves are 2–5 cm long and form a rosette – all are linear with in-rolled margins and broad bases. Flowers open only for part of one day. Flowers July–August.

1.

2

3

4

5

6

H Mason.

PLATE 26 IRIDACEAE

1 **Engysiphon longitubus** *Lewis*
Derivation: Name of uncertain derivation; longitubus (Latin), long tubed.
Distribution: Clanwilliam to Piketberg, Malmesbury and Darling.
Leaves not pleated. Flowers nearly regular with very long tube. The bracts subtending the flower are green – especially in the lower half. Three style branches. Flowers in late spring.

2 **Homoglossum priorii** *N. E. Br.*
Derivation: Homoios (Greek), similar; glossa (Greek), a tongue – referring to the shape and colour of the perianth lobes; priorii – named after R. C. Alexander Prior, a plant collector who visited the Cape in the mid-19th century.
Common Name: Rooi Afrikaner.
Distribution: South western Cape.
The lowest leaf completely ensheaths all the others which have very short blades. The perianth tube is straight and smooth. Flowers in May.

3 **Watsonia marginata** *(L. f.) Ker*
Derivation: Named by P. Miller, the gardener at the Chelsea Physic Garden in honour of Dr. W. Watson, a London apothecary; marginata (Latin), referring to the thickened leaf margin.
Distribution: South western Cape.
Watsonia flowers are usually large and the style is typically six branched. In this species upper part of the perianth tube is funnel-shaped and the stamens are symmetrically arranged inside the flower with small staminodes between each. Flowers in October.

4 **Watsonia hysterantha** *Mathews and L. Bol.*
Derivation: Hysterantha (Greek), flowering when the leaves are dead.
Common Name: Rooipypie or Suikerkan.
Distribution: Saldanha Bay area.
The perianth tube is cylindrical in the upper part and the stamens are arched under the upper perianth lobe. Flower stems stout and up to 1 m. This species flowers in early winter before the leaves develop. Flowers May–June.

5 **Watsonia humilis** *Mill.*
Derivation: Humilis (Latin), short, humble.
Distribution: Western Cape.
One of the shortest of Watsonia species, found throughout the western Cape in moist semi-marshy conditions. The colour varies from pale pink to mauve or purple. Flowers in spring.

1

2

3
x ¼

4

5

H Mason

PLATE 27 IRIDACEAE

1 & 2 **Moraea tripetala** *(L. f.) Ker*
Derivation: Named after Robert More, squire of Shrewsbury in the 18th century – Linnaeus, in his original description, misspelt the name; tri (Latin), three; petala (Latin), petals.
Common Name: Iris.
Distribution: South western Cape to Calvinia and George.
Flowers in clusters on the flower stalk, opening one at a time and very short-lived. The flower has three style branches which are crested. The stigma, a small flap on the lower side of the style branch. The inner perianth segments are reduced to minute cusps or are wanting. This plant is common on the sandy flats. Flowers August–September.

3 & 4 **Moraea fugax** *(de la Roche) Jacq.* (= *M. edulis.*)
Derivation: Fugax (Latin), fleeting, ephemeral.
Common Name: Uintjie or Soetuintjie.
Distribution: South western and southern Cape.
Stems are naked below with one or two long leaves arising below the inflorescence. Flowers sweet-scented; mauve or white; inner perianth segments slightly smaller. The corm is edible. Flowers September–October.

5 **Moraea bellendeni** *(Sweet) N. E. Br.*
Derivation: Named after J. Bellenden-Ker, a botanist who published extensively – particularly on the Iridaceae in the 19th century.
Common Name: Geel Uintjie; Patrysuintjie.
Distribution: South western Cape.
Spathes acute with the upper half brown and membraneous. The inner perianth segments are much smaller and differ from the outer ones, being three-forked. Tips of outer perianth segments are in-curved. Leaves are glabrous. Flowers September–October.

6 **Moraea ciliata** *(Thunb.) Ker*
Derivation: Ciliatus (Latin), ciliate, with small hairs or cilia.
Distribution: South western Cape to Namaqualand and Great Karoo.
Leaves ciliate at the edges. Spathes arising from a tuft of leaves. Perianth lilac, red or yellow. The form illustrated is typical of Darling area ans has a broad style-crust and inner perianth segments. Flowers in spring.

1.

Hmason   4

2

3

6   5

PLATE 28 IRIDACEAE

1 **Geissorhiza monantha** (*Thunb.*) *Eckl.*
Derivation: Geisson (Greek), a tile; rhiza (Greek), a root – referring to the regular overlapping and splitting of the corm tunic in some species; monanthus (Greek), one-flowered.
Distribution: Confined to the Darling and Mamre area.
A tall slender plant, blue with a transparent centre. Flowers in spring.

2 **Geissorhiza juncea** (*Link.*) *A. Dietr.*
Derivation: Junceus (Latin), rush-like.
Distribution: Cape Peninsula, north to Malmesbury and Clanwilliam.
Stems and leaves are glabrous. The flower colour is very variable from white, cream to pale yellow. Outer lobes often pink, red or reddish-brown below. Flowers in spring.

3 **Geissorhiza aspera** *Goldb.*
Derivation: Aspera (Latin), rough.
Common Name: Sysie.
Distribution: Common on flats and low hills from Calvinia to Riversdale and Humansdorp.
Stem coarse; flowers clear blue. Perianth funnel-shaped with a short tube. Flowers August–October.

4 **Geissorhiza rochensis** *Ker*
Derivation: Named after D. de la Roche, an 18th century French plant collector.
Common Name: Kelkiewyn; or red, white and blue.
Distribution: Malmesbury, Darling and Paarl.
Leaves glabrous; perianth tube shorter than spathe. Flower in spring.

5 **Babiana pulchra** (*Salisb.*) *Lewis*
Derivation: From Babianer, Afrikaans for baboon; pulcher (Latin), beautiful.
Distribution: South western Cape sandveld, not extending to the Peninsula.
This beautiful species is polymorphic. Flower colour varies from pale blue to yellow or cream with dark markings on the base of the segments. Flowers most often twisted to one side of the inflorescence. The perianth tube is also slightly curved and twisted. The form illustrated here is found in the Darling district. The flowers are irregular but the perianth lobes are equal. Flowers August–September.

Freason.

PLATE 29 IRIDACEAE

1, 2 & 3 **Gladiolus carinatus** *Ait.*
Derivation: Gladiolus (Latin), a small sword referring to the shape of the leaves in some species; carinatus (Latin), keeled.
Common Name: Mauve Afrikaner or Sandpypie.
Distribution: All along west coastal region to Cape Peninsula and eastern Cape Province, chiefly on the sandy flats.
The lowest of the three true leaves has a blade longer than the flower spike. Flowers vary greatly in colour from mauve, pink to blue or brownish-yellow. Perianth tube curved and the lobes unequal. Flowers July–August.

4 **Gladiolus pillansii** *Lewis*
Derivation: Named in honour of Mr. N. S. Pillans (1884–1964), a well-known Cape botanist who worked at the Bolus Herbarium.
Distribution: Vanrhynsdorp through to Bredasdorp.
Flower stem very slender. There are three narrow leaves. Flowers April–May.

5 & 6 **Gladiolus punctulatus** *Schrank*
Derivation: Punctulatus (Latin), minutely dotted.
Common Name: Pypie.
Distribution: Frequent, from Malmesbury, Worcester, the Peninsula to Caledon.
Flowers pale to darker pink with darker streaks on the three lower lobes. 30–60 cm tall. Flowers July–September.

Sandveld fynbos

1.

2

3

4

5

6

Anason.

PLATE 30 IRIDACEAE

1 Gladiolus alatus *L.*
Derivation: Gladiolus (Latin), small sword; alatus (Latin), winged.
Common Name: Kalkoentjie.
Distribution: From Cape Peninsula up to Namaqualand.
Plant about 20 cm tall with large irregular orange flowers. Flowers August–September.

2 Gladiolus alatus *L.* var. meliusculus *Lewis*
Derivation: Melius (Latin), better; -culus (Latin), diminutive.
Distribution: Darling area only.
A large pink-flowered form. Flowers August–September.

3 Gladiolus angustus *L.*
Derivation: Angustus (Latin), narrow.
Distribution: Occasional in damp places and streams on the sandy flats from Cape Peninsula to Malmesbury.
Tunics (brown scaly portions) on the corms are united leaves linear. Flowering stems up to 1 m tall, perianth segments acute. Perianth lobes much shorter than the tube. Flowers October–November.

4 Gladiolus orchidiflorus *Andr.*
Derivation: Orchidiflorus (Latin), flowers orchid-like.
Common Name: Groen Kalkoentjie.
Distribution: Namaqualand to Darling.
As in *G. alatus*, flowers are very irregular, perianth segments all with a long narrow claw. Flowers are strongly scented. Flowers in spring.

Flowers on the seashore at Buck Bay

1

2

3

H Mason   4

PLATE 31 IRIDACEAE

1 **Gladiolus gracilis** *Jacq.*
Derivation: Gracilis (Latin), thin; slender.
Distribution: Heidelberg (Cape) to Malmesbury.
The leaves are glabrous and very narrow, almost round, and those up the stem have free blades.
The lower leaf sheaths are not mottled. Flowers in August.

2 **Gladiolus caryophyllaceus** (*Burm. f.*) *Poir.*
Derivation: Caryophyllaceus (Latin), like a carnation – referring to the scent.
Distribution: From Calvinia south to the Berg River.
Large-flowered, tall plant with a rich scent. Grows only in coarse sandy soil. Flowers August–
September.

3 **Gladiolus tenellus** *Jacq.*
Derivation: Tenellus (Latin), slender.
Common Name: Botterlelie or Freesia.
Distribution: Bredasdorp to Ceres.
A strongly scented flower. The plant grows in moist or marshy areas. The flower illustrated
is the smaller variety which flowers early in August, known locally as the Botterlelie. The
larger variety which flowers later (September/October) is not recognized by botanists as being
in any way different but is locally considered so, and called the Freesia.

4 **Moraea neglecta** *Lewis*
Derivation: The specific name refers to the fact that a plant as large and conspicuous as this
one remained botanically undescribed until mid-20th century.
Common Name: Geel uintjie.
Distribution: South western Cape to southern part of Namaqualand.
This Moraea differs from one similar in appearance by having white pollen and brown streaks
on the honey guide. Flowers in October.

84

Reeds on Berg River near Kersefontein

1. H. Mason   1.   4   3   2

PLATE 32 IRIDACEAE

1 **Antholyza plicata** *L. f.*
Derivation: Anthos (Greek), a flower; eyssa (Greek), rage – referring to the mouth of the flower being open like an enraged animal; plicatus (Latin), folded into pleats.
Common Name: Hanekam.
Distribution: West coast from Elands Bay to Stompneus Bay.
A spectacular plant with crimson red flowers. Common on the coastal sand dunes among the bushes. Flowers twisted so that pollen is easily deposited on visiting birds attracted by the nectar. Flowers July–October.

2 **Chasmanthe floribunda** *(Salisb.) N. E. Br.* var. **duckittii** *Lewis*
Derivation: Chasme (Greek), gaping; anthos (Greek), flower; floribundus (Latin), profusely flowering; the variety's name honours the Duckitt family of Darling who for three generations have guarded, conserved, loved and studied the wild flowers of the Darling district.
Distribution: Confined to the Darling district.
Perianth tube long; curved with the upper part wide and the lower part very narrow. Lobes unequal; upper arched and lower much shorter and recurved. Stamens and style arched under upper lobe. The spikes are twenty–thirty – flowered, and the flowers are arranged up the spike in two rows. This variety is always yellow-flowered. Flowers July.

3 **Chasmanthe floribunda** *(Salisb.) N. E. Br.*
Derivation: See above.
Common Name: Piempiempie.
Distribution: Vanrhynsdorp to Cape Peninsula.
The normal orange-flowered form. Flowers June–September.

1.

H mason

2

3

PLATE 33 IRIDACEAE

1 **Antholyza ringens** *L.*
Derivation: Anthos (Greek), a flower; eyssa (Greek), rage; ringens (Latin), gaping.
Common Name: Rotstert.
Distribution: South western Cape to Clanwilliam.
The top of the flower stalk is bare except for a few bracts. The flowers which are arranged in two rows at right angles to the erect stalk face upwards. Sunbirds perch on the tough "bird perch" and with their long beaks easily reach the nectar in the base of the flowers. Flowers in spring.

Die Hoog Klip, Paternoster Bay

PLATE 34 ORCHIDACEAE

A family of world-wide distribution, many tropical. Many are hybridized and cultivated as prize greenhouse flowers the world over. There are 20 000 known species belonging to more than 700 genera. Many are terrestrial and some epiphytic. The flowers are most exceptional in appearance and very intricate in structure. Stamens, pistil and part of one of the petals are fused to form a complex structure, the column.

1 **Bonatea speciosa** *Willd.*
Derivation: Named on honour of M. Bonat, professor of botany at Padua; speciosus (Latin), showy, splendid.
Distribution: Malmesbury to the eastern Cape Province and Natal.
Stout plant up to 1 m tall with large green and white flowers. Grows in semi-shade in sand with thick leaf mould covering. Flowers in October.

2 **Herschelia barbata** *(L. f.) Bolus*
Derivation: Named in honour of Sir John Herschel, astronomer at the Cape; barbatus (Latin), bearded.
Distribution: Rare in the south western Cape.
Stems slender, reed-like. Sepals free with the odd one superior and shortly spurred. The lip is lacerated. Characteristically this species has white flowers with blue veins and only a few flowers per spike. Flowers in September–October.

3 **Herschelia lacera** *(Sw.) Lewis*
Derivation: Lacerus (Latin), lacerated.
Distribution: Eastern Cape Province to Sandveld.
45–75 cm tall with grasslike basal leaves. Spike bears four to fifteen flowers and large pale blue flowers with darker blue veins (similar to Plate 34: 2). Flowers November–January.

4 **Disa draconis** *(L. f.) Sw.*
Derivation: Dis (dives) (Latin), rich – thought to be the origin, named especially for the beauty of *Disa uniflora*; draconis (Latin), like a dragon.
Distribution: Southern Namaqualand, Clanwilliam, Worcester to Stellenbosch and Cape Peninsula.
Stem stout, 25–45 cm tall. Two to four basal leaves, absent or dead at flowering time. Grows in sandy places. Flowers November–December.

5 **Pterygodium caffrum** *Sw.*
Derivation: Pterygodes (Greek), wing-like; caffrum, from caffraria.
Common Name: Moederkappie.
Distribution: South western Cape to Knysna.
Leaves green, basal and cauline. Odd sepal and petals joined, lip broad, bilobed with crenulate margin; appendage of lip square concave. The flowers are characteristically bright yellow. Flowers October–December.

6 **Corycium excisum** *Lindley*
Derivation: Coros (Greek), helmet; excisus (Latin), cut out.
Distribution: Clanwilliam to the Cape Peninsula and Bredasdorp.
Erect herb, 5–10 cm tall. Spikes are dense and many flowered with strong scent. Deep hood formed by concave petals and sepals. Flowers in spring.

1

2

3

4

H Mason

5

6

PLATE 35 ORCHIDACEAE

1 **Satyrium carneum** *R. Br.*
Derivation: Satyrus (Latin), satyr; carneus (Latin), flesh-coloured.
Distribution: South western Cape.
The largest *Satyrium*, chiefly in low-lying sandy areas. Flowers September–October.

2 **Corycium crispum** *Sw.*
Derivation: Coros (Greek), helmet; crispus (Latin), crisped, waved.
Distribution: Cape Peninsula to Clanwilliam.
Leaf margins undulated or crisped. Flowers September–October.

3 **Disa macrantha** *Bolus*
Distribution: Cape Peninsula (rare) to Malmesbury.
The distinction between this plant and *D. cornuta* is very slight; when this genus is revised these species will undoubtedly be amalgamated. Currently it is thought that they represent extremes in variation. *D. macrantha* has a more open head than *D. cornuta* and the lip is more pointed with a less solid marking. The bracts are not quite as long as the flowers. Flowers in November.

4 **Disa macrantha** *Bolus*
Same as above.

5 **Disa cornuta** *(L.) Sw.*
Derivation: Cornutus (Latin), horn-shaped.
Distribution: Mamre; throughout the Cape Peninsula and along the coastal area to Port Elizabeth.
The spike of this species is denser than *Disa macrantha*. The hood of the flower is a uniformly deep velvety purple. Flowers October–December.

1

2

3

4

5

H...son.

PLATE 36 ORCHIDACEAE

1 **Pterygodium catholicum** *(L.) Sw.*
Derivation: Pterygodes (Greek), wing-like; catholica (Latin), widespread, general.
Common Name: Moederkappie, Oumakappie.
Distribution: Tulbagh to Swellendam.
The plant is several-flowered. The lip-appendage is triangular with a toothed or barbed margin. Flowers are usually yellow or green but turning red with age. Flowers August–November.

2 **Corycium microglossum** *Lindl.*
Derivation: Corys (Greek), a helmet; micros (Greek), small; glossa (Greek), tongue.
Distribution: Cape Peninsula, Tulbagh and Malmesbury.
The sepals wither soon after the flowers open (and so do the leaves) but the lip remains green. Flowers in November.

3 **Disperis cucullata** *Sw.*
Derivation: Dis- (Greek), twice; pera (Greek), pouch; cucullatus (Latin), hooded.
Distribution: Cape Peninsula to Malmesbury, Paarl and Clanwilliam.
Leaves ovate and green on lower surface. Plants are glabrous. The odd sepal which is posterior has a highly ascending rounded sac. Large green flowers. Flowers in September.

4 **Disperis villosa** *Sw.*
Derivation: Dis- (Greek), twice; pera (Greek), a pouch; villosus (Latin), with soft hairs.
Distribution: Clanwilliam to Cape Peninsula.
Plant small – up to 15 cm tall. Stem is hairy and the leaves are heart-shaped. The small flowers have a rather unpleasant smell. A putative natural hybrid between this species and *D. cucullata* is known from the Darling district. Flowers August–September.

5 **Disperis circumflexa** *Durand and Schinz*
Derivation: Circumflexis (Latin), bent round.
Distribution: Saldanha Bay, Tulbagh to Cape Peninsula.
Leaves glabrous and lance-shaped. Bracts leaf-like, encircling the ovary. Lateral sepals divaricate, spurred in the middle. Flowers August–October.

6 **Satyrium coriifolium** *Sw.*
Derivation: Named after Satyr, the devil with two horns; corium (Latin), skin, leather; folium (Latin), a leaf.
Common Name: Ewwa-trewwa; Ouma Trewwa.
Distribution: Albany to Tulbagh.
Up to 40 cm tall. One to two short basal leaves with several cauline leaves. Yellow, orange to flame-coloured flowers. Flowers July–October.

7 **Satyrium bicorne** *Thunb.*
Derivation: Bicornis (Latin), having two horns.
Distribution: South western Cape to Tulbagh.
Two basal leaves adpressed to the ground and unequal in size. Flower stalk clothed with two to four leaf-like sheaths. Flowers fragrant and pale ochre yellow. Flowers September–November.

1.

2

3

4

4

5

6

7

H Mason

PLATE 37 ORCHIDACEAE

1 **Bartholina burmanniana** (*L.*) *Ker*
Derivation: Named in honour of Thomas Bartholinus (1655–1738), a 17th-century Danish botanist; the species honours Johannes Burmann (1707–1779), professor of botany at Amsterdam University, a friend of Linnaeus.
Common Name: Spider orchid.
Distribution: Grahamstown to Malmesbury.
Hairy plant with one leaf flat on the ground. The lip is divided into many parts. Introduced into gardens in England in 1787 by F. Masson, a gardener, sent out by Kew to collect at the Cape. Flowers August–October.

2 **Satyrium striatum** *Thunb.*
Derivation: Striatus (Latin), marked with fine linear markings.
Distribution: Hermanus to Hopefield.
One radical leaf flat on the ground. Bracts between flowers broad but shorter than the flowers. Spurs very short, the odd sepal is obtuse and well hooded. Flowers September–October.

3 **Schizodium flexuosum** *Lindl.*
Derivation: Schizein (Greek), to split; flexuosus (Latin), bent alternately in opposite directions, zigzagging (referring to the stem).
Common Name: Ham-and-eggs or Eggs-salt-and-pepper.
Distribution: Cape Peninsula to Malmesbury, Tulbagh and Calvinia.
Three sepals, white; the lateral ones spreading. Lip is yellow. Flowers September–October.

4 **Schizodium obliquum** *Lindl.*
Derivation: Obliquus (Latin), oblique.
Distribution: Cape Peninsula to Tulbagh.
Common but difficult to see because they grow amongst the reedy Restionaceae. This genus is very distinct in that the slender stem is wiry, usually with a few right-angled bends near the base. The leaves always form a basal rosette. In this species the flowers are pinkish and the base of the spur is constricted. Flowers in August.

5 & 6 **Schizodium cornutum** (*L.*) *Schltr.*
Derivation: Cornutus (Latin), horn-shaped.
Distribution: Cape Peninsula to Clanwilliam, Calvinia and Bot River.
Plant about 20 cm high. Two to three pale lilac to rose-pink flowers. The lateral sepals are long, narrow and pointed. Grows in damp places. Flowers July–September.

7 **Disa tenella** (*L. f.*) *Sw.*
Derivation: Tenellus (Latin), delicate.
Distribution: Tulbagh, Cape Peninsula to Uitenhage.
Small plant 5–13 cm. Several erect, spirally twisted green leaves. Flowers small and sweetly scented. Flowers August–September.

8 **Pterygodium volucris** (*L. f.*) *Lindl.*
(*Ommatodium volucris.*)
Derivation: Pterugodes (Greek), wing-like; volucris (Latin), a bird or flying insect.
Distribution: Cape Peninsula to Clanwilliam.
There is one spreading basal leaf and one or two cauline leaves. Flowers with an unpleasant heavy scent. Flowers September–October.

9 **Pterygodium catholicum** (*L.*) *Sw.*
See Plate 36: 1.

PLATE 38 PROTEACEAE

A large family of about 1 400 species. It occurs almost entirely in the southern hemisphere. Although several members of the Proteaceae are trees of the tropics and sub-tropics, the Cape species are mainly shrubby.

1 **Protea repens** (*L.*) *L.*

Derivation: Proteus (Greek); the genus *Protea* takes its name from the Greek god Proteus, son of Neptune, who was able to assume different shapes at will; repens (Latin), creeping (when first described this species was erroneously thought to have a creeping habit).
Common Name: Suikerkan; Suikerbos.
Distribution: Widespread throughout the Cape coastal belt from Nieuwoudtville to Grahamstown. An erect shrub 2–3 m in height. Inflorescences white or pink with sticky or glutinous bracts. Often found growing in dense communities, but now much reduced by agricultural development. *P. repens* was cultivated in Europe as early as 1774. Flowers mainly April–October.

2 **Protea scolymocephala** (*L.*) *Reich.*

Derivation: Scolymos (Greek), a thistle; cephale (Greek), a head.
Common Name: Witskollie.
Distribution: Cape coastal belt, Citrusdal to Hermanus.
A small rounded shrub, up to 1 m in height. This species was introduced into Europe in 1780 and soon became a favourite subject in the conservatories of wealthy collectors. Occurs mainly in sandy areas. Flowers June–October.

3 **Protea pulchra** *Rycroft*

Derivation: Pulcher (Latin), beautiful.
Distribution: South western Cape, from Tulbagh to Franschhoek.
A compact to spreading shrub, 1,5 m in diameter. It is common on the sandy flats around Dassenberg and Katzenberg. Several colour forms are known in which the bracts range from creamy-green to various shades of pink. The bracts sometimes have a fringe of black hairs at the apex. Flowers June–October.

4 **Protea odorata** *Thunb.*

Derivation: Odoratus (Latin), scented.
Distribution: South western Cape, near Kalabaskraal and at Hercules Pillar near Durbanville.
A small straggling shrub to 1 m. It has the smallest flowerheads of all the Proteas. This rare species was cultivated in England as early as 1805 by Lee and Kennedy in their nursery at Hammersmith. Flowers March–July.

5 **Protea acaulos** (*L.*) *Reich.*

Derivation: Acaulis (Latin), stemless.
Distribution: South western Cape, Clanwilliam to Swellendam and Bredasdorp.
A dwarf shrublet with tufted or shortly trailing stems. Occasional in sandy soil near Kalabaskraal and Dassenberg. Regenerates from basal stems after burning. Flowers September–November.

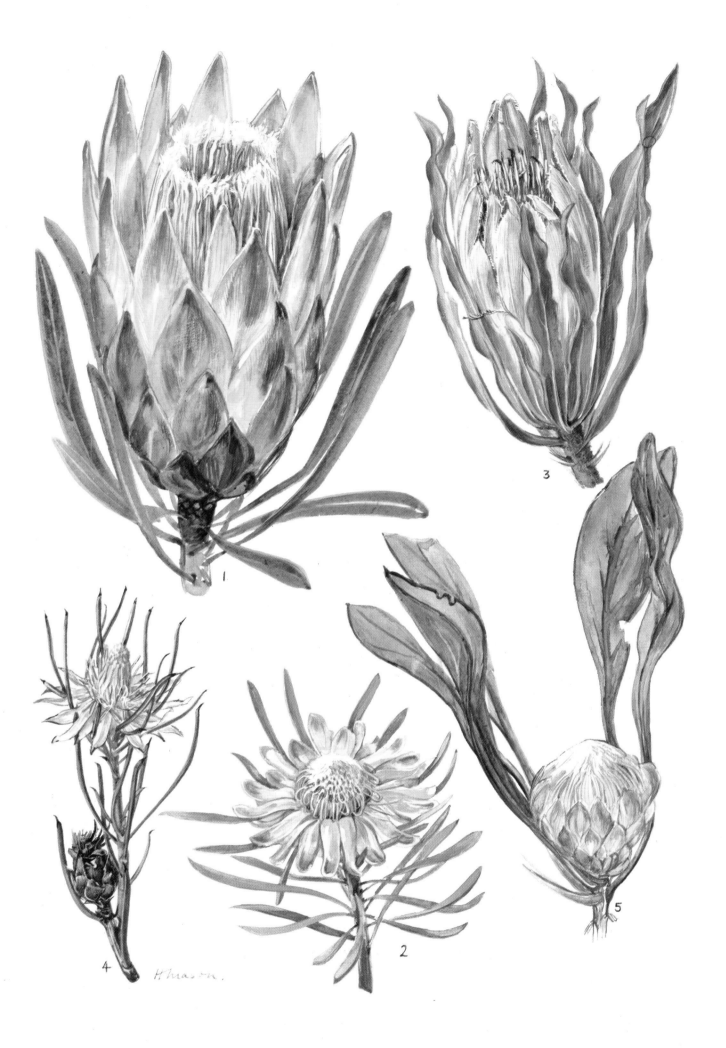

1

3

4   H. Mason.

2

5

PLATE 39 PROTEACEAE

1 **Serruria linearis** *Salisb. ex Knight*
(= *S. simplicifolia* R. Br.)
Derivation: Serruria – after J. Serrurier, professor of botany at Utrecht in the early 18th century; linearis (Latin), linear.
Distribution: Sandy flats between Kalabaskraal, Katzenberg and Dassenberg.
A sparse shrub with a few slender erect stems to 50 cm in height arising from a persistent, subterranean rootstock. This species is unusual in the genus in that the leaves are nearly all acicular-linear while most other species of *Serruria* have dissected leaves. Flowers August–January.

2 **Serruria decipiens** *R. Br.*
Derivation: Decipiens (Latin), deceiving – an allusion to its similarity to *S. adscendens* R. Br.
Distribution: Western Cape coastal flats from Melkbos to Piketberg.
An erect shrub up to 1 m, occasionally growing in dense stands. Bracts and perianths very hairy. Flowers August–November.

3 **Serruria burmannii** *R. Br.*
Derivation: Burmannii – after Johannes Burmann (1707–1779), physician and botanist of Amsterdam.
Distribution: Widespread throughout the western and southern Cape.
A sprawling shrub up to 50 cm in height. Flowers clustered in small insignificant heads, pale pink to carmine; hairy or glabrous. Flowers erratically from May–December.

4 **Diastella proteoides** *(L.) Druce*
Derivation: Diastellein (Greek), to put asunder, separate or expand – alluding to the deeply divided perianth segments; proteoides (Latin), like a Protea.
Distribution: Flats between Bellville and Kuils River in the south, and Mamre in the north.
A low sprawling shrub forming mats 1 m in diameter and about 30 cm in height. Common on sandy flats. Flowers produced at perimeter of plant on the tips of the flowering branches from August–February.

5 **Leucospermum parile** *(Salisb. ex Knight) Sweet*
Derivation: Leucos (Greek), white; sperma (Greek), a seed; parilis (Latin), equal – an allusion to its similarity to other species.
Distribution: Malmesbury district, where it is very local and restricted to sandy areas around Dassenberg and Kalabaskraal.
An erect, rounded shrub up to 1 m in height. The involucral bracts are characteristically glabrous, membranous and subsquarrose, dull carmine or greenish. The flowers are very sweetly scented. *L. parile* was grown and flowered in George Hibbert's conservatory at Clapham, England, in 1805. Flowers August–November.

6 **Leucospermum hypophyllocarpodendron** *(L.) Druce*
Derivation: Hypo (Greek), below; phyllon (Greek), leaf; carpos (Greek), fruit; dendron (Greek), tree; the tree with fruits below the leaves – (an allusion to the position in which the inflorescences are borne).
Common Name: Luisie.
Distribution: South western Cape.
Prostrate shrub with trailing stems and secund leaves. Leaves variable in form, linear and channelled or oblanceolate and flat; softly pubescent at some stage of their growth, some forms loosing their pubescence later. Fire resistant – new shoots regenerate from subterranean rootstock. Sweetly scented flowers. Flowers July–December.

7 **Leucospermum calligerum** *(Salisb. ex Knight) Rourke*
Derivation: Leucos (Greek), white; sperma (Greek), a seed; calligerum (Latin), bearing a callus (referring to the thickening of the leaf apex).
Distribution: South western Cape, Calvinia to Albertinia.
A semi-erect to sprawling shrub, up to 1,5 m in diameter. Inflorescences pale creamy-green on opening becoming dull pink to camine with age. Sweetly scented. Occasional on gravel hills near Malmesbury. Flowers August–November.

8 **Leucospermum rodolentum** *(Salisb. ex Knight) Rourke*
Derivation: Rhodos (Greek), rose; olens (Latin), smelling.
Distribution: South western Cape, Clanwilliam to Worcester.
A large erect shrub 2–3 m in height. Leaves greyish-white. Common in sandy areas around Hopefield. Very sweetly scented. This species was cultivated in conservatories in England as early as 1790. Flowers August–October.

1.

8

5

4

2

7

6

3

H Mason

PLATE 40 PROTEACEAE

1, 2 & 3 **Leucadendron thymifolium** *(Salisb. ex Knight) Williams*
Derivation: Leucos (Greek), white; dendron (Greek), a tree; thymum (Latin), the herb Thyme; folium (Latin), leaf.
Distribution: Malmesbury district, on gravelly hills and flats.
An erect slender stemmed shrub to 1,5 m in height. The male and female flowers are produced mid-August–September. After pollination the cones develop, reaching maturity January–February. (1) Female flower. (2) Male. (3) Mature female cone.

4 **Leucadendron corymbosum** *Berg.*
Derivation: Corymbosus (Latin), with flowers in a cluster.
Distribution: Malmesbury district, Paarl and Worcester districts.
A slender erect shrub up to 2 m, with sparsely branched stems and a dense basal tuft of foliage. Occasionally in heavy clay near Mamre Road Station. Male and female flowers produced mid-October–mid-November. Mature female cones depicted.

5, 6 & 7 **Leucadendron salignum** *Berg.*
Derivation: Salignus (Latin), willow-like.
Common Name: Knopbos; Tolbos.
Distribution: Cape coastal belt, Nieuwoudtville to Grahamstown.
An erect to sub-erect shrub up to 1 m. Fire resistant but new stems regenerating from an underground rootstock after a veld fire. Involucral leaves green becoming yellow or yellow flushed with red in the flowering period. Male flowers yellow or red. The most ubiquitous species of *Leucadendron.* Very common in sandy areas. Flowers May–September according to locality. (5) Mature female cone. (6) Open male flowers. (7) Male flowers in bud.

8 & 9 **Leucadendron cinereum** *(Solander ex Ait.) R. Br.*
Derivation: Cinerus (Latin), ash grey.
Common Name: Vaalknopbos; Tolbos.
Distribution: Western Cape coastal districts of Malmesbury, Hopefield and Piketberg.
An erect shrub to 2 m in height. Leaves greyish or silvery. An exceptionally silvery leaved form occurs near Ysterfontein. Flowers September–November. The cones mature in February. (8) Male flowers. (9) Mature female cone.

1. ♀   2. ♂   3. ♀   4. ♀   5. ♀   6. ♂   7. ♂   8. ♂   9. ♀

Hmason.

PLATE 41 AIZOACEAE

A family of dicotyledons; 165 genera and about 2 500 species – found mainly in South Africa but also in Australia, California and South America. Leaves usually fleshy and opposite or alternate. Three, five or more stamens and sterile stamens (staminodes). The ovary chambers may also number three, five or many; with one to many seeds per locule. The shape and structure of the fruit is important in the classification of the genera.

1 **Ruschia concinna** *L. Bol.*
Derivation: Named in honour of Herr E. Rusch, a farmer in Lichtenstein near Windhoek, S.W.A.; concinnus (Latin), well put together; pleasing.
Distribution: Between Malmesbury, Hopefield and Darling.
Ruschias are closely related to *Lampranthus* but differ in having the chambers of the fruit more or less closed at the mouth by a tubercle. Stamens and staminodes form a cone. Leaves have a bristle at the apex. Flowers in July.

2 **Lampranthus citrinus** *(L. Bol.) L. Bol.*
Derivation: Lampros (Greek), shining; anthos (Greek), a flower; citrinus (Latin), lemon yellow.
Distribution: Darling, Malmesbury area, Stompneus to Kalabaskraal.
A loosely branched shrub up to 12 cm. Upper side of leaf flat; lower keeled. Leaves spotted. Flowers solitary. Flowers June–July.

3 **Lampranthus vanputtennii** *(L. Bol.) N. E. Br.*
Derivation: Species' name honours Mr. van Putten who collected it at Lamberts Bay in 1925.
Distribution: Lamberts Bay; Graafwater.
An erect shrub up to 30 cm. Branches thick and stiff. Skin shiny later turning grey. Upper side of leaf flat; back at first rounded and then keeled. Flowers often white towards the centre. Flowers July–August.

4 **Vanzijlia angustipetala** *(L. Bol.) N. E. Br.*
Derivation: Honours Dorothy van Zijl, wife of the Hon. Mr. Justice van Zijl, a keen plant collector; angustipetalis (Latin), with narrow petals.
Distribution: Lamberts Bay, Elands Bay.
Leaves united for quarter to half of their length; slightly keeled with a recurved tip. Flower solitary. Flowers in July.

5 **Cheiridopsis inspersa** *N. E. Br.*
Derivation: Cheiris (Greek), a sleeve; opsis (Greek), like; some species, however, do not have the characteristic sleeve of leaves; inspersus (Latin), dispersed.
Distribution: Common round Saldanha Bay.
Plants almost stemless, leaves fused at the base, flat on the upper surface and bluntly keeled at the back near the tip, this outer surface being crowded with whitish dots. Leaves bright red in spring. Flowers March–June.

6 **Ruschia tecta** *L. Bol.*
Derivation: Tectus (Latin), covered, hidden.
Distribution: Melkbosch, Mamre, Tulbagh, Vredenburg.
A stiff glabrous shrub. Leaves fused at base to form long, narrow sheath marked with a deep groove along the fusion line. Flowers in October.

7 **Erepsia carterae** *L. Bol.*
Derivation: The specific name honours Miss B. Carter, an artist at the Bolus Herbarium.
Distribution: Ceres to Darling.
Closely related to *Lampranthus*. The stamens are completely hidden, but the flowers remain open day and night. Flowers February–March.

8 **Lampranthus aduncus** *(Haw.) N. E. Br.*
Derivation: Aduncus (Latin), hooked.
Distribution: South western Cape.
Branches erect, curved and grey-skinned. Leaves crowded at the tip of the branches; recurved at the tip. Flowers solitary and terminal. Flowers May–July.

PLATE 42 AIZOACEAE

1 **Lampranthus aureus** (*L.*) *N. E. Br.*
Derivation: Aureus (Latin), golden yellow.
Common Name: Vygie.
Distribution: Saldanha Bay, Vredenburg.
Branches dark brown. Leaves green with lighter dots (almost transparent). Flowers August–September.

2 **Cephalophyllum vanputtenii** *L. Bol.*
Derivation: Named in honour of Joost van Putten who lived near the coast at Lambert's Bay; his property being called Van Putten's Vlei.
Distribution: West coastal area.
Flowers in September.

3 **Lampranthus argenteus** *L. Bol.*
Derivation: Argenteus (Latin), of the colour of silver.
Distribution: Malmesbury to Clanwilliam.
Flowers in October.

4 **Apatesia helianthoides** (*Ait.*) *N. E. Br.*
Derivation: Apatesis (Greek), deception, alluding to the resemblance (before flowering) to *Hymenogyne*; helianthoides (Greek), like *Helianthus*, the sun flower.
Common Name: Vetkousie.
Distribution: Cape Peninsula, Paarl to Saldanha Bay.
Annuals. Styles united at the base. Flowers July–September.

5 **Conicosia pugioniformis** (*L.*) *N. E. Br.*
Derivation: Konikos (Greek), conical; pugioniformis (Latin), dagger-shaped.
Common Name: Gansie.
Distribution: Mamre to Vanrhynsdorp.
Leaves reddish at the base. Lower pair of leaves larger with axillary branches bearing smaller leaves. Flowers August–September.

6 **Drosanthemum floribundum** (*Haw.*) *Schwant.*
Derivation: Drosos (Greek), dew; anthemon (Greek), a flower; floribundum (Latin), many flowers.
Distribution: Cape Peninsula, Villiersdorp, Worcester to Elands Bay.
Perennial shrubs with creeping branches which root at the nodes. Leaves very slightly joined at base. Flowers with four to seven styles. Usually on brack soil. Flowers September–October.

7 **Disphyma crassifolium** (*L.*) *L. Bol.*
Derivation: Dis (Greek), double; phuma (Greek), tubercle; crassus (Latin), thick; folius (Latin), leaf.
Distribution: South western Cape.
A creeping succulent, readily rooting at the nodes. Leaves covered with transparent dots. Flowers in October.

8 **Lampranthus vernalis** *L. Bol.*
Derivation: Vernalis (Latin), vernal.
Distribution: Mamre to Saldanha Bay.
Leaves shortly mucronate and triangular at the base. Flowers in groups of three. Flowers in September.

9 **Mesembryanthemum alatum** (*L. Bol.*) *L. Bol.*
Derivation: Mesembria (Greek), midday; anthemon (Greek), a flower; alatus (Latin), winged.
Distribution: Piketberg, St. Helena, Saldanha.
Stem short with creeping branches; six-angled with two angles broadly winged. Leaf martins undulate, leaves glandular and slightly sticky. Shrub grows up to 70 cm high and 60 cm in diameter. Flowers September–November.

PLATE 43 AIZOACEAE

1 **Carpobrotus sauerae** *Schwant.*
Derivation: Karpobrotus (Greek), with edible fruit. Species honours a Miss Sauer, who first collected the plant.
Common Name: Elandsvy.
Distribution: Darling, Langebaan and Saldanha Bay.
Numerous petals. Ovary is inferior. Ten or more styles. Fruit succulent. This species has the largest flowers. The fruit is eaten when succulent and ripe. Flowers in spring.

2 **Lampranthus filicaulis** (*Haw.*) *N. E. Br.*
Derivation: Lampros (Greek), shining; anthos (Greek), a flower; fili- (Latin), thread; caulis (Latin), stem.
Distribution: Cape Peninsula to Saldanha Bay.
This plant grows in damp areas. Branches very slender; rooting at the nodes. Flowers solitary and terminal on a stalk. Flowers in August.

3 **Dorotheanthus bellidiformis** (*Burm.*) *N. E. Br.*
Derivation: Named in honour of Dr. Schwantes' mother, Dorothea; anthos (Greek), a flower; the specific name means "the English daisy" *Bellis perennis.*
Common Name: Bokbaai Vygie.
Distribution: Cape Peninsula to Saldanha Bay.
Plants grown in cultivation under the name *Dorotheanthus bellidiformis* are usually a mixture of it and the following species. Flowers August to September.

4 **Dorotheanthus oculatus** *N. E. Br.*
Derivation: Oculus (Latin), eye.
Distribution: Calvinia, Elands Bay to Mamre.
Annual herb, shiny and glandular. Leaves spathulate to long with acute tips. Anthers and stigmas always red. Flowers in September.

5 **Sphalmanthus canaliculatus** *N. E. Br.*
Derivation: Sphalma (Greek), a mistake; anthos (Greek), a flower; mistakenly regarded as a species of Mesembryanthemum.
Distribution: Western Cape coast, Cape Peninsula, Southern Cape coast.
Succulent perennial, papulose on all green parts, rootstock tuberous or fleshy. It favours sandy places, and the edges of beaches. Flowers September to November.

6 **Drosanthemum intermedium** (*L. Bol.*) *L. Bol.*
Derivation: Drosos (Greek), dew; anthemon (Greek), a flower; intermedius (Latin), intermediate.
Distribution: Saldanha Bay to Mossel Bay.
Stems slender and creeping, nodes thickened. Leaves with shiny fluid-filled papillae. Flowers single on stalks. Flowers November–February.

7 **Ruschia diversifolia** *L. Bol.*
Derivation: Diversifolius (Latin), with leaves of different shapes.
Distribution: Western and south western Cape, from Clanwilliam to Tulbagh.
Semi-erect with trailing stems. Occasional on hills around Darling. Flowers May–July.

8 **Ruschia pulchella** (*Haw.*) *Schwant.*
Derivation: Pulcher (Latin), beautiful.
Distribution: Cape Peninsula, Stellenbosch, Malmesbury to Constable Hill (Langebaan).
Trailing plants, spreading over flat rock surfaces. Flowers July–August.

2

1.

3

4

3

8

6

7

5

HMason

PLATE 44 AIZOACEAE

Flowers illustrated on this plate belong to a section of the Aizoaceae in which the petals are absent.

1 Pharnaceum lineare *L. f.*
Derivation: Named after Pharnaces, a king of Pontus; linearis (Latin), linear.
Distribution: Widespread in sandy areas.
Leaves with stipules and in whorls. The five entire perianth segments are free. Ovary superior. Flowers September–November.

2 Pharnaceum incanum *L.*
Derivation: Incanus (Latin), hoary, white.
Distribution: Widespread in drier areas of the western Cape and Karoo.
Stem woody at the base. The stipules at the base of the leaves form clusters of straight threads. Flowers July–December.

3 Acrosanthes teretifolia *E. & Z.*
Derivation: Acros (Greek), at the top; anthos (Greek), a flower.
Distribution: South western Cape.
Leaves without stipules and opposite. Stamens in groups alternate with perianth segments. Ovary superior. One ovule in each ovary chamber. Flowers throughout the spring and summer.

4 Limeum africanum *Burm.*
Derivation: Loimos (Greek), a plague; africanus (Latin), of Africa.
Distribution: South western Cape.
A procumbent annual. Perianth segments green with a white edge. Reported to be poisonous. Flowers August–September.

5 Aizoon nigrescens *E. & Z.*
Derivation: Aei (Greek), always; zoos (Greek), alive; nigrescens (Latin), becoming black (when dried).
Distribution: Clanwilliam to Mamre.
Ovary inferior; 8 or more stamens. Flowers in terminal clusters on creeping stem, and as solitary axillary flowers. Flowers in September.

6 Aizoon paniculatum *L.*
Derivation: Specific name refers to the arrangement of the flowers.
Distribution: Cape Peninsula; Piquetberg to Clanwilliam.
Leaves narrow. Flowers pink in a terminal group. Flowers September–October.

H Mason

PLATE 45

LORANTHACEAE

The mistletoe family is found in tropical and temperate regions; 300 species distributed in 36 genera. These plants are either parasites attached to woody hosts or in cases where they have green leaves only semi-parasites. The fruits are fleshy and colourful, and are distributed by birds.

1 Loranthus glaucus *Thunb.*
Derivation: Loros (Greek), strap; anthos (Greek), a flower, alluding to the shape of the sepals; glaucos (Latin), grey-green.
Distribution: From western to central Cape.
This belongs to a genus of semi-parasites, found widely in the tropics and subtropics. Leaves glaucous. Corolla covered with flat scales. Flowers February–April.

2 Viscum rotundifolium *L.f.*
Derivation: Viscum (Latin), mistletoe; rotundus (Latin), almost circular; folium (Latin), leaf.
Common Name: Mistletoe, Voëlent.
Distribution: Rare in the Sandveld and Cape Peninsula but frequent in the eastern Cape Province and right up to tropical Africa.
Stems jointed, green and 10–30 cm long. Flowers in groups of three, the central flower being male and the lateral ones female. Petals of female flower greenish, male yellowish. Berries bright yellow to red, ripe in January–February.

3 Viscum capense *Thunb.*
Derivation: Capense, of the Cape.
Distribution: Widespread in the Cape.
Leaves very reduced, i.e. only small projections at the joints. Flowers solitary. Fruit white, 5–9 mm in diameter. Flowers mainly June–October.

CHENOPODIACEAE

120 genera and about 1 400 species world-wide in distribution, particularly in salty areas, the members being halophytes. Since the presence of salt necessitates a reduction in transpiration they all exhibit xerophytic features.

4 Arthrocnemum perenne *(Mill.) Moss*
Derivation: Arthron (Greek), a joint; kneme (Greek), a limb; perennis (Latin), perennial.
Distribution: Frequent in tidal marshes.
Branches shiny yellowish-green and very fleshy. Flowers in groups of three on a spike 2–3 cm long. Flowers April–June.

5 Arthrocnemum capense *Moss*
Derivation: Capense (Latin), of the Cape.
Distribution: Frequent along the coast on dunes and in tidal marshes.
Plants prostate, woody at the base. The branches do not all end in inflorescences. Flowers in groups of three to five. The stamens appear after the stigmas. Flowers in March.

6 Chenolea diffusa *Thunb.*
Derivation: Chen (Greek), a goose; olea (Latin), olive; diffusus (Latin), diffuse.
Distribution: Found on rocks extending into the sea-spray zone; rarely on sand.
Stems often red. Leaves grey with silky hairs. Flowers February–April.

7 Salsola kali *L.*
Derivation: Salsus (Latin), salty; kalium (Latin), potassium.
Common Name: Russian thistle or Tumble weed: Saltwort.
Distribution: A native of Asia, now world-wide in distribution. It was probably introduced to South Africa during the Anglo-Boer War.
Stems fluted. Leaves and bracts are spine-tipped. Perianth segments hard and brown or straw-coloured, red when fruiting. Parts of mature plants easily broken off in high wind and blown over the veld. The ashes of this plant are used as a source of very impure carbonate of soda called Barilla, which is used in soap and glass making. Flowers in April.

H. Mason

PLATE 46

CARYOPHYLLACEAE

Eighty genera and 1 300 species world-wide with a high proportion in Britain. Mainly herbs, but with a great variation in growth habit and type of flowers. The carnation is the best known of the garden flowers of this family.

1 **Dianthus albens** *Sol.*
Derivation: Dios (Greek), divine, noble; anthos (Greek), a flower, i.e. the divine flower; albens (Latin), whitened.
Distribution: Widespread at low altitudes.
Stems perennial and woody. Leaves rough at the edges. Flowers November–March.

2 **Silene undulata** *Ait.*
Derivation: Sialon (Greek), saliva (these plants are always sticky); undulatus (Latin), undulate.
Common Name: Job se kraaltjies.
Distribution: Widespread.
Plants sticky; leaves distinctly undulate; flowers white to pink, arranged in dichotomous cymes. Flowers July–October.

3 **Silene clandestina** *Jacq.*
Derivation: Clandestines (Latin), hidden.
Distribution: Widespread throughout South Africa.
An annual. Flowers stalked, petals bifid with a fairly prominent corona or crest, Calyx hairy. Flowers September–November.

MENISPERMACEAE

A family of 65 genera and 350 species from warm temperate areas; represented in South Africa by only three genera. The flowers are usually unisexual.

4 **Antizoma capensis** (*Thunb.*) *Diels*
Derivation: Anti (Greek), opposite; zoma (Greek), a covering; capensis (Latin), of the Cape.
Common Name: Davidjies.
Distribution: Widespread.
A climbing or twining, sprawling shrub, poisonous to stock. Young stems white and hairy. The small flowers with 4 green petals are in clusters of two to six. Flowers February–May.

FUMARIACEAE

Sixteen genera and 450 species found in especially warm temperate areas. Leaves alternate and flowers very irregular – closely related to the Papaveraceae.

5 **Cysticapnos vesicarius** (*L.*) *Fedde*
Derivation: Cystis (Greek), a bladder; kapnos (Greek), smoke; vesicarius (Latin), bladder-like; inflated.
Common Name: Klappertjies.
Distribution: Widespread.
A trailing climber with a watery juice in the stems. Fruit inflated. Flowers August–September.

1.

H Mason

4

5

2

3

PLATE 47 CRUCIFERAE

Two hundred and twenty genera and nearly 9 000 species, world-wide in distribution but common in the Mediterranean regions. A natural and well-defined family. There are always four petals and six stamens, the latter arranged in two whorls of four and two. The fruit is very characteristic of the family, it is a type of pod known as a siliqua.

1 Heliophila coronopifolia *L.*
Derivation: Helios (Greek), the sun; philos (Greek), loving; coronopi (Latin), buckhorn; folium (Latin), leaf; coronopifolia (Latin), with leaves like *Coronopus*, the Crow Foot.
Common Name: Wild flax.
Distribution: Caledon to Vanrhynsdorp.
A glabrous branching annual. Leaves simple, 20–60 cm tall. Flowers 1,8 cm across, pale to bright blue with a white or pale yellow centre, without stipules. Margins of the fruit constricted between the seeds. The species is variable and the plants in the Malmesbury district are much larger and taller than those on the Cape Peninsula. Flowers August–October.

2 Heliophila *sp.*
Without mature fruits this plant cannot be identified.

3 Heliophila acuminata *(E. & Z.) Steud.*
Derivation: Acuminatus (Latin), pointed.
Distribution: From Vanrhynsdorp, Calvinia to the Cape Peninsula.
An annual. Leaves without stipules. Flowers white or bright blue. Flowers August–September.

3B Heliophila digitata *L. f.*
Derivation: Digitate (Latin), having fingers.
Distribution: From Clanwilliam, through the Cape Peninsula to Riversdale.
An annual up to 50 cm tall, stems often reddish or brown at the base. Flowers colour pink to blue. The fruits have straight margins. Flowers in spring.

4 Heliophila africana *(L.) Marais*
Derivation: Africanus (Latin), of Africa.
Common Name: Flax.
Distribution: Robertson, Cape Peninsula to Vanrhynsdorp.
An annual, usually 60–70 cm tall, slightly hairy or glabrous. Leaves very variable, from long simple and narrow to irregularly lobed or short and broad. Each petal with one or rarely two appendages, as illustrated. Flowers August–October.

H Mason.

PLATE 48 CRASSULACEAE

Thirty-five genera and 1 500 species, mainly South African. Most are perennial, often found in dry rocky places exhibiting xerophytic characteristics. The carpels are free.

1 Cotyledon orbiculata *L.*
Derivation: Cotyle (Greek), a cup, referring to the basal rosette of leaves often being cup-like; orbicularis (Latin), circular.
Common Name: Honde-oor, Varkoor, Kouteri, Vaalblaar (in Darling district only).
Distribution: Widespread in the Cape.
C. I. Latrobe, the German missionary, who was at the Cape from 1815–1816 mentions these cotyledons growing round Mamre in his "A Journal of a Visit to South Africa".
A variable species. Stem branched and habit bushy. Leaves 8 cm long and 5–10 cm wide, narrowing at the base and covered with a powdery white substance. Reported to be poisonous. Flowers December–January.

2 Cotyledon grandiflora *Meisn.*
Derivation: Grandiflorus (Latin), with large flowers.
Distribution: Widespread in coastal scrub. Occasional on dry rocky slopes.
Plant up to 2 cm high. Stem decumbent, thick and fleshy covered with leaf bases. The leaves dry off in summer. Peduncle erect bearing red or yellow, red-streaked flowers. Flowers January–February.

3 Crassula natans *Thunb.*
Derivation: Crassus (Latin), thick; natans (Latin), swimming or floating.
Common Name: Miggiegras, Meeugras.
Distribution: Widespread throughout the Cape in marshy places.
A slender flacid straggling annual, the basal parts sometimes perennial. Leaves bright green and flat. Internodes longer than the leaves. Flowers in groups of two or three in axils of leaves. Petals white, often with a red blotch on the back. Flowers July–October.

4 Crassula brachyphylla *Adamson*
Derivation: Brachyphyllus (Greek), short-leaved.
Distribution: Widespread in muddy pools or vleis.
A glabrous annual often growing in hemispherical clusters. Leaves fall when plant is flowering. Petals white or pale pink. United leaves or bracts found at the base of the flower stalk. Flowers October.

5 Crassula scabra *L.*
Derivation: Scaber (Latin), scabby, rough.
Distribution: Cape Peninsula–Ceres.
Small branched semi-succulent plant with the stems and fleshy leaves covered with small, narrow white reversed scales. Inflorescence loosely capitate. Petals white. Flowers November–January.

PLATE 49 CRASSULACEAE

1 **Cotyledon paniculata** *L. f.*
Derivation: Paniculata (Latin), referring to the panicled arrangement of the flowers.
Common Name: Botterblom, Botterboom (in Darling district).
Distribution: Malmesbury, Cape Peninsula and the Karoo.
Leaves alternate, falling off with onset of summer. Stem erect and stout.
Corolla tube less than 2,5 cm. Flowers November–December.

2 **Vauanthes dichotoma** *(L.) O. Kuntze*
Derivation: The letter "v"; anthos (Greek), a flower; dichotomos (Greek), divided in two.
Distribution: South and south western Cape.
A South African genus with one annual species only. Flowers red, orange or yellow. Common in low-lying sandy areas. Flowers October–November.

3 **Crassula incana** *E. & Z.*
Derivation: Crassus (Latin), thick; incanus (Latin), quite grey, hoary.
Distribution: West coast to the drier interior of the Cape.
A tallish plant with slender stems often minutely downy. Leaves convex below. Petals gradually tapering into a channelled point. Flowers in January.

4 **Crassula capensis** *(L.) Bail.*
Derivation: Capensis (Latin), of the Cape.
Common Name: Cape Snowdrop, Melk barroe, Lily of the valley.
Distribution: South western Cape.
A tuberous perennial. Flowers in terminal clusters. Ripe ovaries red. Flowers May–August.

Verloren Vlei, Elands Bay

1.

1.

2

3

2

4

PLATE 50

DROSERACEAE

Four genera and 150 species. The genus *Drosera* is world-wide but others are restricted in their distribution. Plants are usually found in acid bogs – they have a perennial rhizome with rosettes of leaves. All are insectiverous with sticky tentacles on their leaves.

1 Drosera cistiflora *L.*

Derivation: Droseros (Greek), dewy; cistiflora – *Cistus*-flowered – from ciste (Greek), a box, in reference to the form of the seed vessel in the flower of the genus, *Cistus*.
Common Name: Sundew, Sondou, Snotroos, Slakroos, Vlakroos.
Distribution: Caledon to Hopefield.
A dwarf form with few leaves on the flowering stem, referred formerly to *D. zeyheri*, now included under *D. cistiflora L.* Rarely found except in recently cleared or burnt sites. Flowers in September.

2 Drosera pauciflora *Banks ex DC.*

Derivation: Pauciflorus (Latin), with few flowers.
Common Name: Sundew, Sondou, Snotroos, Slakroos, Vlakroos.
Distribution: South western Cape. Common round Darling, Paarl, Stellenbosch.
Plants have few swollen roots and form tufted rosettes of leaves. The flower stalk is leafless. Petals more than 8 mm long – always with a dark blotch at the base. Flowers white, rose-pink or lilac. Flowers August–November.

3 Drosera cistiflora *L.*

Derivation: Droseros (Greek), dewy; cistiflora, shaped like the flower of the genus *Cistus*.
Distribution: Common from Namaqualand to Port Elizabeth.
In this species the basal rosette of leaves may be less pronounced, the flowering stalk bearing long narrow leaves with long, knob-bearing tentacles. One to several flowers on the stalk, white, yellow, pink, mauve or purple, often with a deep green centre. The dark red flower illustrated is peculiar to the Malmesbury area. Petals always notched at the apex. Flowers August–September.

ROSACEAE

One hundred genera and 2 000 species of trees, shrubs and herbs found all over the world. Leaves alternate with stipules – often fused to the leaf. Some members of the family have male and female flowers on different plants.

4 Grielum humifusum *Thunb.*

Derivation: Humifusus (Latin), spread out over the ground.
Distribution: Kimberley, Calvinia to Malmesbury.
Flowers smaller than *G. grandiflorum*, which is also found in this area. Stems trailing, leaves green and divided. (*G. grandiflorum* grey and more finely divided.) Flowers open in bright sunlight only. Fruits spiny. Flowers August–September.

4

2

1

2

3

H Mason

PLATE 51

BRUNIACEAE

Twelve genera and 75 species all South African. Heath-like shrubs common in the fynbos. Flowers very small, arranged in capitate clusters.

1 Berzelia abrotanoides (L.) Brongn.

Derivation: Named in honour of Berzelius, a Swedish chemist. This species bears a superficial resemblance to another genus *Abrotanum*.

Common Name: Rooibeentjies.

Distribution: South western Cape; especially in marshy places.

A shrub up to 1 m tall. The minute sepals adhere to the ovary. The flower-heads 6–9 mm wide. Leaves up to 5 mm long. The bright red swellings on the peduncles are characteristic. Flowers August–September.

2 Berzelia lanuginosa (L.) Brongn.

Derivation: Laniger (Latin), wool-bearing.

Common Name: Kolkol.

Distribution: Giftberg to Breede River.

A slender shrub about 1,5 m tall: found along streamsides and in marshy places with perennial underground water. Leaves needle-like. Flower heads about 5 mm, globose. Flowers July–November.

3 Staavia radiata (L.) Dahl

Derivation: Named in honour of Martin Staaf, a correspondent of Linnaeus; radiatus (Latin), radiate, bearing rays like a daisy.

Common Name: Altydbos.

Distribution: Coastal belt from Malmesbury to Knysna.

A shrub usually 60–80 cm tall. Involucral bracts radiate; flowers arranged on a flat daisy-like disc. Flowers throughout the year.

SAXIFRAGACEAE

Thirty genera and 580 species mainly north temperate. Perennial herbs with alternate and exstipulate leaves.

4 Montinia caryophyllacea Thunb.

Derivation: Named after L. Montin (1723–1785), a Swedish botanist; caryon (Greek), nut kernel; -phyllon (Greek), leaf.

Common Name: Peperbos.

Distribution: Widespread in the Cape.

An erect shrub up to 1,5 m tall. Flowers October–May.

SANTALACEAE

Thirty genera and 400 species, tropical and temperate in distribution. Semi-parasitic shrubs, trees and herbs.

5 Thesidium fragile Sond.

Derivation: The little *Thesium*; fragilis (Latin), brittle.

Distribution: Swellendam to Malmesbury.

An erect branched shrub, 40 cm tall. Male and female plants dissimilar, the female illustrated. Characteristically the ripe fruit is bright red, seated on a fleshy cup-like base. Leaves minute. Flowers August–November.

6 Thesium virgatum Lam.

Derivation: Generic name origin obscure; virgatus (Latin), twiggy, long and slender.

Distribution: Knysna to Malmesbury.

Much branched and erect. Lower leaves needle-shaped and up to 3 cm long. Upper ones much smaller. Flowers in small clusters. Flowers in July.

7 Colpoon compressum Berg.

Derivation: Generic name of uncertain origin; compressus (Latin), laterally flattened.

Distribution: Common throughout the south western and southern Cape.

A large shrub to 3 m. Usually found in sandy coastal areas. The flowers and fruits are produced erratically throughout the year, but mainly from June to December.

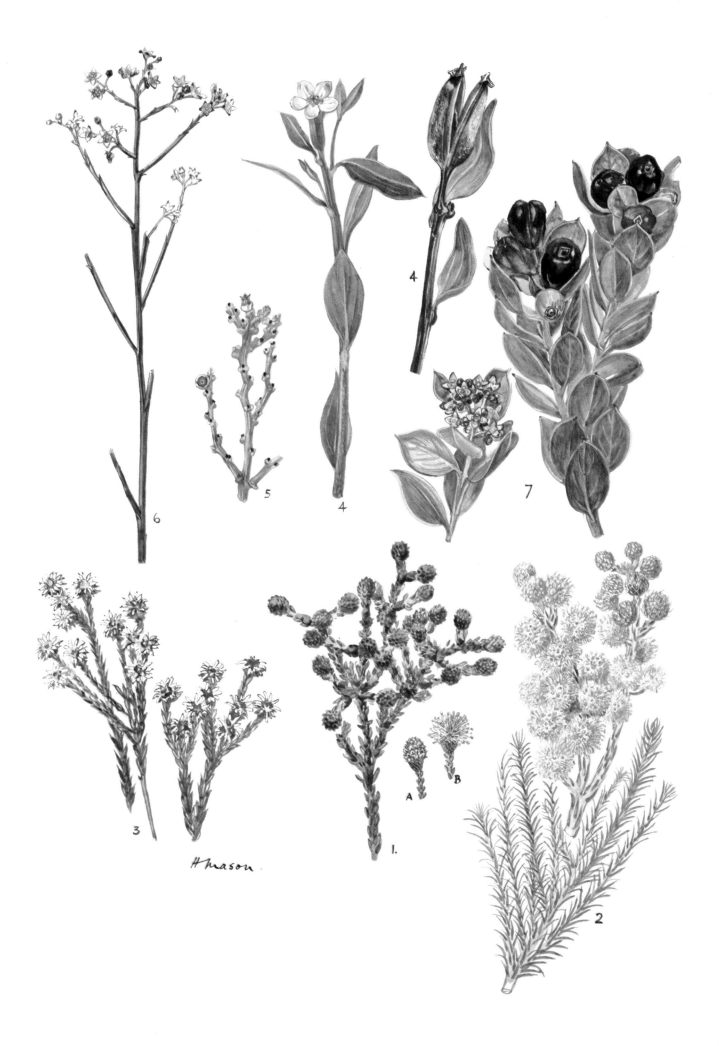

H Mason.

PLATE 52 LEGUMINOSAE

The third largest family of flowering plants with about 600 genera and 12 000 species found all over the world in every soil type in every climate. Growth forms from trees to water plants, 100 genera are found in South Africa. The roots usually have growths on them which contain a bacterium, Rhizobium, which is capable of converting atmospheric nitrogen into a nitrate which is easily used by the plant. Leguminous plants do much to improve poor soils. The family is divided into three very distinct groups:

Mimosoideae – to which all the invasive Australian Acacias at the Cape belong.

Caesalpinioideae – The plants in this group have large irregular flowers. Found mainly in tropical regions.

Papilionoideae – to which group all the pea-like flowers belong and the only group illustrated here.

1 **Aspalathus linearis** (*Burm f.*) *R. Dahlgr.* ssp. **latipetala** *R. Dahlgr.*
Derivation: Aspalathos (Greek), a scented shrub (strangely though, only a few species have a scent); linearis (Latin), linear; latipelalus (Latin), with broad petals.
Common Name: Rooibostee.
Distribution: Bredasdorp to Malmesbury.
A shrub up to 2 m. Leaves simple. Flowers usually solitary. Plants found in the Malmesbury area have smaller flowers than those nearer the Cape Peninsula. Flowers November–March.

2 **Aspalathus pinguis** *Thunb.* ssp. **occidentalis** *R. Dahlgr.*
Derivation: Pinguis (Latin), fat; fatty; occidentalis (Latin), western.
Distribution: Hopefield to Piquetberg.
Occurs, usually, in mixed renoster veld. Leaflets fascicled, pedicels short. Flowers May–December.

3 **Aspalathus spinosa** *L.* ssp. **spinosa**
Derivation: Spinosus (Latin), spiny.
Distribution: Widespread in Cape extending to Natal.
A shrub up to 2 m tall. Spines longer than leaves. Older flowers have a red mark on the petals. A very variable species. Flowers August–April.

4 **Aspalathus quinquefolia** *L.* ssp. **quinquefolia**
Derivation: Quinquefolius (Latin), with five leaves.
Distribution: Flat sandy lowlands from the Cape Peninsula to Malmesbury.
A creeping shrub only 20 cm tall; much branched at the base. Leaflets small – larger on the upper part of the branches. Flowers in dense terminal heads. Flowers August–November.

5 **Amphithalea ericaefolia** *E. & Z.*
Derivation: Amphithales (Greek), flowering round the branch; ericaefolius (Latin), with erica-like leaves.
Distribution: In sheltered kloofs from Cape Peninsula to Malmesbury.
A shrub up to 1,5 m tall, with simple leaves, silver-grey up to 9 mm long. Leaves silky-silvery and strongly revolute. Flowers December–June.

6 **Cyclopia genistoides** (*L.*) *R. Br.*
Derivation: Kuklos (Greek), a circle; pous (Greek), a foot – referring to the circular base of the calyx; like *Genista* – a plant commonly known as the broom, a name used by Virgil.
Common Name: Bossiestee; Heuningtee, Bush tea.
Distribution: Frequent on the hilly slopes in the south western Cape.
A woody shrub between 30–70 cm tall. Leaflets narrow and very revolute. Leavy twigs are fermented, dried and then used as tea. Flowers July–December.

H Mason

PLATE 53 LEGUMINOSAE

1 **Podalyria sericea** *R. Br.*
Derivation: Podalyrius – a son of Aesculapius; sericeus (Latin), silky, with long straight close-pressed glossy hairs.
Distribution: South western Cape.
A small shrub having a silvery lustre. Flowers pink, arising singly in the leaf axils. Flowers May–August.

2 **Dipogon lignosus** *(L.) Verdecourt (=Dolichos gibbosus* Thunb.)
Derivation: Dipogon (Greek), two beards; lignosus (Latin), woody.
Common Name: Ertjiebos.
Distribution: From Sandveld to the eastern Cape.
A climber. Leaves trifoliate with small stipules. Flowers pink or purple. Stems often spirally twisted. Flowers August–January – sometimes all year.

3 **Lotononis prostrata** *Benth.*
Derivation: A combination of *Lotus* and *Ononis* – two genera of the Leguminosae; prostratus (Latin), on the ground.
Distribution: Clanwilliam to George.
Many slender creeping branched stems. Leaves trifoliate and silky. Calyx sepals unequal; the lateral ones more or less united and the top one longer. Flower in the axils of the leaves. Stamens united. Pod swollen; channelled on the upper side. Flowers July–September.

4 **Sutherlandia frutescens** *R. Br.*
Derivation: Named in honour of James Sutherland (died 1719), superintendent of the Royal Botanic Gardens, Edinburgh; frutescens (Latin), becoming shrubby.
Common Name: Kankerbos, in Darling area known as Gansie, Gansbossie or Wildekeurtjie.
Distribution: Widespread in South Africa.
A shrub, varying in size. Ten stamens, diadelphous (nine fused and one free). Style bearded on the upper side. Pods large, inflated and many seeded. Flowers September–February.

5 **Vicia atropurpurea** *Desf.*
Derivation: Vicia (Latin), name for a vetch used by Virgil; atropurpureus (Latin), dark purple; porphyra (Greek), was the original name of a Mediterranean shell-fish used for the manufacture of a purple dye.
Common Name: Wilde ertjie.
Distribution: Introduced from Europe and now widespread on road verges and waste places.
A softly pubescent climbing annual. Stem angular and leaves pinnate, ending in a branched tendril. Flowers clustered. Flowers September–November.

6 **Rafnia angulata** *Thunb.*
Derivation: Named in honour of C. G. Rafu, a Danish botanist of the late 18th century–early 19th century; angulatus (Latin), angled.
Distribution: Cape Peninsula to Malmesbury.
The keel tapers to an acute point with a definite beak. Flowers September–April.

PLATE 54

GERANIACEAE

Five genera and about 750 species found all over the world – about 300 species are found in the Republic.

Many of these plants are aromatic and are still used medicinally. Leaves often with large prominent stipules. The fruits are very characteristic. When ripe a portion of the fruit encloses the seed and a strip of the long style breaks off. The latter portion curls and has projecting hairs, forming a hairy awn. This awn is hygroscopic and with winding and unwinding, when it is wetted by dew or dried, the seed is bored into the ground.

1 **Pelargonium multicaule** *Jacq.*

Derivation: Multicaulis (Latin), many stemmed.

Distribution: Port Elizabeth to Malmesbury – but not on the Cape Peninsula; confined to drier areas.

Stems angular and often glabrous. Sepals shorter than the calyx tube; petals light purple with darker marks. Flowers September–January.

2 **Pelargonium triste** *(L.) Ait.*

Derivation: Tristis (Latin), sad; dull-coloured.

Common Name: Kaneeltjies.

Distribution: South western Cape.

A tuberous plant. Lower leaves arising from a short stem. Flowers hairy, dull yellow with purple markings and seven fertile stamens; sweet-scented at night. Flowers September–November.

3 **Monsonia speciosa** *L.*

Derivation: Lady Anne Vane was the great grand-daughter of Charles II, who, after a divorce in 1757, married Col. George Monson. She was a keen naturalist who, in 1774, went walking to collect wild flowers at the Cape with Thunberg and Masson; this was while she was *en route* to Calcutta to join her husband. She died in 1776. Linnaeus in 1764 wrote her a most interesting "Love Letter" claiming to have been infatuated with her for a long time, although he never met her, and asking if he could name this genus after her "so that your name may be commemorated in the Kingdom of Flora". Speciosus (Latin), beautiful.

Common Name: Sambreeltjie.

Distribution: Caledon, Stellenbosch, Paarl and Malmesbury.

This beautiful species was cultivated in England by 1774 from seed sent from the Cape by the Kew gardener, Francis Masson. Leaves crowded and the petioles much longer than the blades. The flowers of this genus have 15 stamens in 5 bundles of 3. Flowers greenish to white and pink inside with a dark spot at the base. Petals greenish white to bright pink outside. Flowers August–September.

LEGUMINOSAE. See also Plate 52.

4 **Indigofera procumbens** *L.*

Derivation: Indigo is obtained from several species of this large genus – hence the name; procumbens (Latin), prostrate.

Common Name: Lewertjie.

Distribution: Clanwilliam, Worcester, Malmesbury.

Creeping stems – sometimes underground. Three leaflets almost oval. Pods tapering to the base. Flowers June–November.

5 **Lebeckia spinescens** *Harv.*

Derivation: Honours a relatively unknown botanist, Lebeck; spinescens (Latin), spiny.

Distribution: South West Africa down the west coast to Malmesbury and in drier Karoo areas to Aberdeen and the eastern Cape.

A rigid spiny shrub with silky hairs. Leaves on long petioles. Flowers June–September.

1

2

3

4

5

Hma.50

PLATE 55 GERANIACEAE

1 **Pelargonium ferulaceum** *Willd.*
Derivation: Pelargos (Greek), a stork; ferulaceum, like *Ferula* (a genus of the Umbelliferae) – the giant fennel.
Distribution: Saldanha Bay into the Karoo to the eastern Cape Province.
A plant with a succulent stem. Leaves hairy and stipules small and ovate. Two upper petals longer than the others; 5 stamens. Flowers March–May.

2 **Pelargonium senecioides** *L. Her.*
Derivation: Like a *Senecio*.
Distribution: South western Cape.
This plant has no swollen tuber. Stipules free. Calyx segments with dark prominent ribs. Five petals – all more or less equal. Five fertile stamens. Flowers September–November.

3 **Pelargonium longifolium** *Jacq.*
Derivation: Longifolius (Latin), long-leaved.
Distribution: From Clanwilliam to Bredasdorp.
Stemless with a prominent tuber. Leaves varying from simple to deeply and finely divided. Leaves in winter and spring, flowers in summer.

4 **Pelargonium gibbosum** (*L.*) *Ait.*
Derivation: Gibbosus (Latin), unevenly swollen.
Distribution: Widespread in the Cape Province.
Diffuse and glabrous; scrambling amongst bushes. Stem distinctly swollen at the nodes. Five equal narrow petals. Common especially in sandy areas near the sea. Flowers November–April.

5 **Pelargonium hirsutum** (*Burm. f.*) *Ait.*
Derivation: Hirsustus (Latin), hairy.
Distribution: Clanwilliam to Cape Peninsula.
Stem often surrounded by bases of old leaves. Plants forming tubers. Leaves much divided and hairy. Flowers in November.

H mason

PLATE 56 GERANIACEAE

1 Pelargonium myrrhifolium (L.) Ait.

Derivation: Pelargos (Greek), a stork; myrrhifolium (Latin), leaves like the herb, *Myrrhis* (myrrh).

Distribution: Namaqualand, south western and southern Cape to Port Elizabeth and Queenstown.

This plant was first illustrated in European literature in 1678 after it had been successfully introduced into the Leyden Botanic Garden. A creeping plant which makes a good border or rockery subject. Flowers October–December.

2 Pelargonium rapaceum (L.) Jacq.

Derivation: Rapa (Latin), a turnip, alluding to the large root resembling a turnip.

Distribution: South western Cape.

Stems glabrous at the nodes, plants with subterranean tubers. The nectary tube extends almost to the base of the peduncle. Five fertile stamens and five petals. Flowers November–December.

3 Pelargonium fulgidum (L.) Ait.

Derivation: Fulgidus (Latin), shining, bright coloured.

Distribution: South western Cape to Namaqualand.

This plant was in cultivation in Holland in the early 18th century; its cultivation spread to Italy and England. Grows on rocky, exposed windswept areas. Leaves crowded at the end of the branches, sometimes very silvery. Seven fertile stamens. Flowers in June.

4 Pelargonium cucullatum (L.) Ait.

Derivation: Cucullatus (Latin), hooded.

Common Name: Wilde Malfa.

Distribution: South western Cape.

It has been cultivated in Europe since the late 17th century. Up to 1 m tall. Free flowering and, like the former, probably a parent of many of the modern garden hybrids. Leaves very soft with toothed margins. Flowers September–February.

5 Pelargonium capitatum (L.) Ait.

Derivation: Capitatus (Latin), with a knob-like head.

Distribution: South western Cape.

Numerous flowers on short pedicels in dense heads. Upper pink petals veined with purple. Calyx sepals pointed at the tip. Flowers intermittently but mainly in September–November.

6 Geranium incanum L.

Derivation: Geranos (Greek), a crane; incanus (Latin), hoary, white.

Common Name: Horlosies.

Distribution: South western Cape to Natal.

Perennials with leaf segments long and narrow. Petals are notched at the tips. All 10 stamens fertile and bearing anthers. Flower colour varies to a deep mauve lilac. Flowers August–November.

1.

2

3

4

5

6

H Mason

PLATE 57 OXALIDACEAE

Seven genera and 850 species mainly tropical and subtropical, usually perennial herbs. Five petals twisted in characteristic manner. In South Africa this family is found chiefly in the Cape. All the South African species of this genus have bulbs and trimorphic flowers (with either short, medium or long stamens).

1 **Oxalis burtoniae** *Salter.*
Derivation: Oxys (Greek), acid; burtoniae – honours a Mrs. H. Burton, a collector.
Distribution: Recorded only from Langebaan to Paternoster.
Leaves compound, usually with 7 leaflets but always more than 4. Peduncle one-flowered. Petals yellow. Flowers May–June.

2 **Oxalis tenella** *Jacq.*
Derivation: Tenellus (Latin), delicate.
Distribution: Vanrhynsdorp to Saldanha.
Flowers white. Few to many leaves, always 3 leaflets – oval to long and slightly incised at the tip. Flowers May–June.

3 **Oxalis hirta** *L.*
Derivation: Hirtus (Latin), hairy.
Distribution: Widespread in the south western Cape up to Clanwilliam.
A very variable group species. Stem leafy and leaves sessile, trifid. Peduncles arising in the axils of leaves, one-flowered. Flowers light purple to lilac, cream and white. Plants more or less hairy. Flowers April–June.

4 **Oxalis purpurea** *L.*
Derivation: Purpura – the name of a shell-fish from the Mediterranean from which the Phoenicians made their purple dye. Purpureus covers various colours between red and violet.
Distribution: Widespread in the Cape Province.
A very variable species. A stemless plant, robust and often hairy. There are three leaflets, usually glabrous above and often deep purple beneath. Peduncles one-flowered, shorter or longer than leaves. Sepals striated with longitudinal pellucid lines. Corolla 1–4 cm long; light purple, rose, violet, salmon, yellow, cream or white. Flowers April–September. (See Plate 58: 3.)

5 **Oxalis eckloniana** *Presl* var. **sonderi** *Salter*
Derivation: The species' name honours C. F. Ecklon (see Plate 58: 1). The variety honours a German botanist, Dr. O. W. Sonder, a co-author of Flora Capensis, who encouraged and financially assisted Ecklon.
Distribution: Bredasdorp, Caledon, Cape Peninsula to Malmesbury and Clanwilliam.
A variety of a variable species. Two to many leaves. Leaflets sub-rotund, closely or distantly ciliate, often purple underneath. Petals light purple, violet-white or rarely orange. Flowers May–June. (See Plate 58: 1.)

6 **Oxalis luteola** *Jacq.* var. **minor** *Salter*
Derivation: luteolus (Latin), pale yellow.
Distribution: Malmesbury to Vanrhynsdorp.
Young bulbs are viscous with gummy outer covering. Leaves often have purple veins and purple margins. Peduncles one-flowered. Flowers yellow. Flowers May–July.

7 **Oxalis polyphylla** *Jacq.*
Derivation: Polyphyllus (Greek), many leaved.
Distribution: Malmesbury to Port Elizabeth along the coast.
This species shows much variation in the bulb. Stem rigid, up to 20 cm long. Leaves 10–30, apically congested. Usually 3 leaflets (some 5–7) linear, with two orange-red spots at the tip of the leaflets. Flowers rose-pink, light purple or white. Flowers March–June.

8 **Oxalis pusilla** *Jacq.*
Derivation: Pusillus (Latin), very small.
Distribution: Cape Peninsula, Stellenbosch to Langebaan.
Bulb small, smooth, not more than 1 cm long; 6–10 leaves per plant arranged at the top of the stem. Petioles 2–3 times as long as the leaflets. Three leaflets, linear and sessile. Peduncle one-flowered. Petals white to pale rose with a wide funnel-shaped yellow tube, rarely with a purple eye. Flowers May–July.

9 **Oxalis eckloniana** *Presl* var. **hopefieldiana** *R. Kunth*
Derivation: The variety comes from Hopefield.
Distribution: This variety is found from Mamre to Clanwilliam.
A hairy plant. The 3 leaflets especially hairy along the midrib on the underside of the leaf, which is often purple in colour. Many small bulbils are produced on underground creeping stems. Flowers vary in colour from light purple to orange. Flowers in May. See Plate 57: 5.

1.

1.

2

3

3

3

3

4

5

6

7

8

9

1.

H.Mason

PLATE 58 OXALIDACEAE

1 **Oxalis eckloniana** *Presl*
Derivation: Name honours Christian Friedrich Ecklon (born in South Jutland 17.12.1795; died in Cape Town 9.10.1868), an apothecary and botanical collector. In 1823 he came to the Cape as assistant to the apothecary Polemann and spent his spare time collecting plants. In about 1829 he formed partnership with another collector, K. L. P. Zeyher.
Distribution: Cape Peninsula to the Piketberg area.
Leaflets obovate and more or less equal in size. Petals yellow. Flowers in May.

2 **Oxalis pusilla** *Jacq.*
Description: See Plate 57: 8.

3 **Oxalis purpurea** *L.*
Derivation: Purpureus (Latin), purple.
Distribution: Darling to Piketberg.
A widespread species with large leaves, usually spreading and ciliate at the margins, often purple beneath. This particular yellow form is confined to a small area. Other forms have white or pink corollas. Flowers April–September. (See Plate 57: 4.)

4 **Oxalis dregei** *Sond.*
Derivation: Honours Johan Franz Drège (born in Altona near Hamburg, Germany, 25.3.1794–died in Altona 3.2.1881), a botanical collector and traveller who received horticultural training in Göttingen. He came to the Cape in 1826 to join his brother, Carl Friedrich, a physician, with whom he travelled and collected. Drege's specimens were handed over to Ernst Meyer, professor of botany at Köningsberg.
Distribution: Namaqualand to the Berg River.
Found in marshy areas. Leaves 6–12, each with one leaflet only; blade usually deeply incised. Petals white but forming a broad tubular area which is yellow. Flowers May–September.

5 **Oxalis obtusa** *Jacq.*
Colour Form. (See Plate 58: 9.)

6 **Oxalis hirta** *L.* var. **tenuicaulis** *Kunth*
Derivation: Hirtus (Latin), hairy; tenuicaulis (Latin), with a slender stem.
Distribution: Malmesbury, particularly Hopefield and Darling.
This variety is taller and more slender than the typical form. Corolla white to very pale pink. Flowers in April. (See Plate 57: 2.)

7 **Oxalis hirta** *L.* var. **tubiflora** *Salter*
Derivation: Tubiflorus (Latin), with tubular flowers.
Distribution: Vanrhynsdorp, Piketberg to Kalabaskraal.
A rigid erect plant. Corolla light purple with a tube 2–3 times as long as the lobes. Flowers in April.

8 **Oxalis flava** *L.* form G. (i) according to Salter
Derivation: Flavus (Latin), yellow.
Distribution: This species is widely distributed in the Cape Province but the form illustrated is confined to the Hopefield-Langebaan area.
Leaflets 1–5, with definite cartilaginous margins. Flowers yellow. Flowers in August.

9 **Oxalis obtusa** *Jacq.*
Derivation: Obtusus (Latin), obtuse; blunt.
Distribution: Widespread in the Cape.
Usually ten to twenty leaves, but sometimes up to sixty, congested at the stem apex. The flower stalks bearing distinct opposite bracts. Corolla pink, brick red or pale yellow, often purple veined on the reverse. Double flowers are produced. Flowers June–October.

H mason

PLATE 59 ZYGOPHYLLACEAE

Twenty-five genera and 240 species, tropical and subtropical. Mostly woody perennials. Leaves usually fleshy or leathery with stipules.

1 Zygophyllum fulvum *L.*
Derivation: Fulvus (Latin), dull tawny yellow.
Distribution: South western and southern Cape.
Small shrub. Leaves bifoliate, sessile. Flowers dull tawny yellow with a red blotch at the base of the petal. Flowers July–October.

2 Zygophyllum sessilifolium *L.*
Derivation: Sessilifolius (Latin), with sessile leaves (without a leaf stalk).
Distribution: Cape Peninsula, Ceres, Vanrhynsdorp.
Stems slender, woody and prostrate at the base. Leaves fleshy, and flat. Stipules small and reflexed. Flower stalks longer than the leaves. Sepals oval and purplish; petals white with purple streaks. Flowers July–September.

3 Zygophyllum flexuosum *E. & Z.*
Derivation: Flexuosus (Latin), zigzag, bent alternately in opposite directions.
Common Name: Spekbossie.
Distribution: Oudtshoorn, Riversdale, Montagu to Vredendal.
A bush up to 1 m tall. Stems angular and pale. Leaves sessile, stalked. Stipules recurved and persistent after the leaves have fallen. Sepals yellow-brown; petals deep yellow with purple blotch. Flowers July–October.

4 Zygophyllum morgsana *L.*
Derivation: The use of the name morgsana as a specific epithet is very interesting and devious. The medieval herbalist, Leonhart Rauwolf (died 1596), reported that the Syrians used a plant which they called Morgsani as a vermifuge for children. This plant, Morgsani, is a *Zygophyllum* currently called *Z. fabago* (a native of Syria). As the Cape species resembled the Syrian one, Linnaeus revived the ancient name morgsana, to indicate this resemblance.
Common Name: Skilpadbos.
Distribution: From Plettenberg Bay to Namaqualand.
An erect shrub up to 80 cm tall. Leaves with short stalk, fleshly, bad smelling when crushed. Flowers in parts of four (4 sepals, 4 petals, etc.). Sepals fringed with hairs and petals usually pale yellow. Seeds winged. Flowers in August.

3

4

2

1.

4

Thos.

PLATE 60 RUTACEAE

One hundred and fifty genera and 900 species – tropical and temperate – found particularly in South Africa and Australia. Trees and shrubs often xerophytes with a heath-like habit. Plants of this family have glands containing volatile oils and many are used medicinally. Citrus yields important fruits. Twenty genera are recorded in the Republic.

1 **Diosma oppositifolia** *L.*
Derivation: Dios (Greek), divine; osme (Greek), odour; oppositifolia (Latin), opposite leaves.
Common Name: Wild Buchu.
Distribution: Riversdale, Cape Peninsula to Malmesbury.
An erect shrub usually less than 1 m high, with opposite leaves. Flowers in terminal clusters, shortly stalked. The ripe fruits (capsules) without horns. Found mainly on the sandy flats. Flowers February–September.

2 **Diosma hirsuta** *L.*
Derivation: Hirsutus (Latin), covered with fairly coarse stiff hairs.
Common Name: Wild Buchu, Kanferbos.
Distribution: Clanwilliam to Bredasdorp.
A diffuse shrub with leaves alternately arranged. The leaves round-backed, slightly channelled above. The capsule having pronounced horns. Flowers February–September.

3 **Diosma dichotoma** *Berg.* (*D. cupressina* L.)
Derivation: Dichotomus (Latin), dividing in pairs.
Distribution: Western Cape Flats to Hopefield.
A small shrub with opposite leaves. Flowers terminal and sessile – one or two together. Capsule without horns. Flowers in January.

4 **Macrostylis villosa** *Sond.* var. **glabrata** *Sond.*
Derivation: Makros (Greek), long; stulos (Greek), a style; villosus (Latin), shaggy with fairly long straight hairs.
Distribution: Cape Peninsula to Mamre.
A shrub up to 50 cm tall. Leaves narrow with a keel on the lower surface – glabrous or hairy. Petals white tinged with pink. Flowers February–April.

5 **Adenandra uniflora** *Willd.*
Derivation: Aden (Greek), a gland; ander (Greek), a man; uniflora (Latin), one flower.
Common Name: China flower; Kommetjie teewater.
Distribution: South western Cape.
A compact shrub with aromatic leaves with revolute margins. Staminodes present and, like the stamens, hairy. Flowers April–November.

6 **Agathosma capensis** *Dümmer*
Derivation: Agathos (Greek), good; osme (Greek), smell; capensis (Latin), of the Cape.
Distribution: Very widespread in the Cape.
This species is very variable with either hairy or glabrous leaves which are often inrolled and keeled. Flower stalks 0,5 cm—1 cm long; petals with distinct claw. Flowers throughout the year.

7 **Coleonema album** *B. & W.*
Derivation: Koleos (Greek), a sheath; nema (Greek), a filament, alluding to the staminodes.
Common Name: Klipbuchu.
Distribution: Widespread along the southern Cape coast, on rocky outcrops.
Flowers solitary in the axils of leaves towards the ends of branches. Stamens 5. Staminodes 5, sheathed in grooves on the faces of the petals. Flowers June–November.

1.

2

3

1.

4

5

6

H Mason

7

PLATE 61

POLYGALACEAE

Ten genera and approximately 700 species found all over the world except in New Zealand and Antarctica. The flowers are two-lipped and in most plants in this family, they resemble the flowers of the pea family.

1 **Muraltia filiformis** (*Thunb.*) *DC.*

Derivation: Named in honour of J. M. Muralt, author of a botanical work published in Zurich in 1576; fili (Latin), thread; forma (Latin), form, shape.

Distribution: Cape Peninsula to Paarl.

Leaves solitary and not spiny. Sepals nearly equal and of similar shape. Seven stamens. Fruits dry, splitting open when ripe. Flowers throughout the year.

2 **Muraltia thunbergii** *E. & Z.*

Derivation: Named in honour of the Swedish plant collector C. P. Thunberg, who was at the Cape from 1772–1775.

Distribution: Cape Peninsula, Paarl, Mamre.

A spreading shrub 10–40 cm high, branching particularly at the base of the plant. Stems very leafy. Flowers longer than 4 mm. Flowers May–June.

3 **Muraltia macropetala** *Harv.*

Derivation: Macropetala (with large petals).

Common Name: Skilpadbos.

Distribution: South western Cape to Saldanha Bay.

A rigid shrub branched at right-angles; stems hairy. Leaves with spiny tips. Most common on west coast. Flowering season confined to spring.

4 **Muraltia brevicornu** *DC.*

Derivation: Brevis (Latin), short; cornu (Latin), horn.

Distribution: Cape Peninsula to Piketberg.

A loosely branched shrub up to 90 cm tall. Branches grooved. Leaves erect; sessile and shortly mucronate. Flowers in spring.

5 **Polygala garcini** *DC.*

Derivation: Polys (Greek), much; gala (Greek), milk – reputed to increase milk yields in cows. *Garcinia*, another plant to which the genus bears a superficial resemblance.

Distribution: Southern sandveld and south western Cape.

Herb up to 40 cm tall; common on sandy areas. Two lateral sepals wing-like and coloured. It is observed that the flowers close at night and in dull weather. Wings (sepals) turn green after flowering and protect the fruit. Flowers from spring to mid-summer.

6 **Mundia spinosa** *DC.*

Derivation: Named after J. L. Leopold Mund, a pharmacist in Berlin who was sent to the Cape in about 1816; spinosus (Latin) thorny, spiny.

Common Name: Duinbessie, Skilpadbessie.

Distribution: Widespread.

Numbers and size of leaves on this shrub vary considerably according to where they grow. Flowers lilac or white. Fleshy red berries eaten by children and birds. Common in sandy places. Flowers May–October.

ANACARDIACEAE

Sixty genera and 500 species mainly tropical but some subtropical. Trees and shrubs. There are resin ducts in the wood but the leaves are not gland-dotted. Many of the tropical genera have edible fruit: *Mangifera indica* (Mango) and *Anacardium occidentale* (cashew nut).

7 **Rhus mucronata** *Thunb.* var. **villosa** (*L. f.*) *Schonl.*

Derivation: The origin of the name is uncertain; mucronatus (Latin), with a point; villosus (Latin), shaggy with soft straight hair.

Common Name: Taaibos, Koerente.

Distribution: Widespread in South Africa but the hairy variety confined to the south western Cape. Common in the Sandveld on the flats and lower slopes.

Leaves three-partite and petiolate with distinct veins. Flowers September–February.

8 **Rhus undulata** *Jacq.*

Derivation: Undulatus (Latin), undulate, wavy.

Common Name: Taaibos, Koerente.

Distribution: South western Cape.

Leaves with fairly long stalk; margins slightly wavy. Flowers April–June.

9 **Rhus dissecta** *Thunb.*

Derivation: Dissectus (Latin), divided.

Distribution: South western Cape.

Leaflets deeply lobed, dark green above and pale green below. Flowers July–November.

144

1.

2.

3.

4.

5.

6.

6.

7.

7.

8.

9.

H mason

PLATE 62 EUPHORBIACEAE

Three hundred genera and about 5 000 species. World-wide except in the arctic regions. Every type of plant growth is found – from creeper to tree to succulent. Many have latex in special lactiferous vessels.

The inflorescence is very complicated. Most of the members of the family are poisonous and a few, like *Hevea*, the rubber plant, are economically important.

1 Euphorbia tuberosa *L.*

Derivation: Name honours Euphorbus Musa, physician to King Juba, king of Numidia *c.* 47 B.C.; tuberans (Latin), becoming swollen or tuberous.

Distribution: Cape Peninsula to Vanrhynsdorp.

Root tuberous and the leaves clustered at soil level. Involucre sessile and cup-shaped. Flowers April–September.

2 Euphorbia mauritanica *L.*

Derivation: Mauritanica (Latin), Mauritania in N.W. Africa, erroneously thought to have originated there.

Common Name: Geel Melkbos.

Distribution: Fairly common all along the Cape coastal areas.

Members of the genus *Euphorbia* all have a milky latex and many are succulent. The involucre is a cup of four or five glands with alternating lobes – each containing several male flowers with a single stamen. Female flowers consist only of a stalked ovary. Flowers August–October.

3 Euphorbia genistoides *Berg.*

Derivation: Genistoides – like the genus *Genista*, a European and Asian genus of Legumes.

Common Name: Pisgoed.

Distribution: Cape Peninsula to Vanrhynsdorp.

The 30 cm tall plants are not succulent. Branches reddish-brown. Leaves with recurved pointed tips. Inflorescence containing flowers of both sexes. Flowers August–September.

4 Euphorbia burmannii *E. Mey.*

Derivation: Name honours Nicholas Lourens Burmann, the younger of two very famous Dutch botanists of the 18th century.

Distribution: Widespread in the Cape.

This shrub is grazed despite its milky latex. On either side of the rudimentary leaves or leaf scars there are two glands. A female plant is illustrated. Flowers July–November.

5 Euphorbia caput-medusae *Lam.*

Derivation: Resembling the head of the Medusa of Greek mythology, whose hair was entwined with serpents.

Common Name: Vingerpol; Noordpol.

Distribution: South western Cape.

A dwarf succulent whose peduncle remains persistently on the branches. It has many tubercled branches. Leaves falling. Flowers July–September.

6 Clutia daphnoides *Lam.*

Derivation: Honours Outger Cluyt, a Dutch botanist of the 17th century; daphnoides (Latin), like the plant *Daphne*.

Distribution: Common along the coast.

A shrub not more than 1 m high and covered with a cream pubescence. No milky latex. Male flowers with four or five glands at the base of the pale green sepals and petals. The female flowers solitary without glands. Flowers June–September.

7 Caralluma incarnata *N. E. Br.*

Derivation: Caraluma, a name lost in obscurity but thought to have been derived from a vernacular name, Car-Allum, used by the Telingas of British India; incarnatus (Latin), flesh-coloured.

Distribution: Namaqualand to Saldanha Bay.

This plant was known in Europe as early as 1738. A bushy plant up to 30 cm tall with erect stems. Flowers foul smelling. Flowers in September. (N.B.: This plant is a member of the family Asclepiadaceae. See Plate 68.)

1.

2

3

4

5

6

7

H. Mason.

PLATE 63
RHAMNACEAE
Fifty-eight genera and about 900 species found all over the world – usually trees or shrubs. Leaves simple, usually with stipules. Flowers are inconspicuous in terminal heads. The genus *Phylica* is almost entirely south western Cape in distribution.

1 **Phylica ericoides** *L.*
Derivation: Phyllicos (Greek), leafy; ericoides (Latin), like Erica, referring to the leaves.
Distribution: South western Cape.
A much branched shrub, 40 cm tall. Leaves small and revolute. Flowers 1–2 mm long. Commonly found near the sea. Flowers April–August.

2 **Phylica stipularis** *L.*
Derivation: Stipularis (Latin), belonging to the stipules.
Distribution: Common on flats, hills and lower mountain slopes in south western Cape.
A much branched shrub, 50 cm tall. Distinguished by the presence of stipules. Flowers clustered into heads. Sepals covered with white woolly hairs. Flowers March–June.

3 **Phylica plumosa** *L.*
Derivation: Plumosus (Latin), feathery.
Distribution: South western Cape.
Branches covered with short and long grey or tawny hairs. Leaves 1–1,5 cm long, with strongly revolute margins. Bracts at the base of the flowers are long, leaf-like and covered on both surfaces with grey or buff hairs. Flowers May–August.

4 **Phylica parviflora** *Berg.*
Derivation: Parviflorus (Latin), with small flowers.
Distribution: South western Cape.
A compact, branched, 40 cm high shrub, with short woolly hairs. Flowers January–May.

MALVACEAE
Seventy-five genera and 1 000 species – tropical and temperate. The leaves are variously lobed with stipules and stellate-shaped hairs. Below the flowers there is usually a cluster of bracts known as the epicalyx.

5 **Anisodontea scabrosa** *(L.) Bates*
Derivation: Anis (Greek), unequal; odont (Greek), teeth; scabrosus (Latin), rough.
Distribution: Widespread.
A perennial, much branched rough shrub up to 1,5 m tall. Flowers August–November.

STERCULIACEAE
Sixty genera and 700 species – chiefly tropical trees, shrubs, herbs and sometimes creepers. Plants of vastly differing appearances and flower structure are found in this family. In the Republic there are six genera.

6 **Hermannia multiflora** *Jacq.*
Derivation: Generic name honours Paul Hermann (1646–1695), professor of botany at Leyden; multiflorus (Latin), with many flowers.
Common Name: Chinese Lantern, Ag-dae-geneesbos.
Distribution: Cape Peninsula, Caledon, Vanrhynsdorp to Calvinia.
This plant is similar to and has been confused with *Hermannia cuneifolia* Jacq. *H. multiflora*, however, has distinct veins on the under-surface of the leaf which also has a whitish tomentum. Calyx hairy or scaly and reddish-brown. Flowers in August.

7 **Hermannia pinnata** *L.* (=*H. diffusa Jacq.*)
Derivation: Pinnata refers to the arrangement of the leaves.
Distribution: South western Cape.
A diffuse creeping herb. Stipules large and leaf-like and with the leaves forming a whorl. Leaves undivided or variously dissected. Sepals with a long free portion above the cup-like base. Flowers April–May.

8 **Hermannia diffusa** *L. f.*
Derivation: Diffusus (Latin), diffuse.
Distribution: Paarl, Malmesbury, Mamre.
A diffuse creeping herb. Stipules simple, leaves very dissected. Flowers April–September.

9 **Hermannia procumbens** *Cav.*
Derivation: Procumbens (Latin), prostrate.
Distribution: South western Cape.
A creeping herb with divided leaves and simple stipules. Flowers all the year.

10 **Hermannia alnifolia** *L.*
Derivation: With leaves like the Alder, genus *Alnus*.
Distribution: Common on the Cape Peninsula to Mamre and eastwards to George.
An erect spreading plant, leaves with prominent veins and white tomentum. Flowers always small and the inflorescence very branched. Flowers August–October.

PLATE 64

PENAEACEAE
Members of this family are found only in the Cape Province; most common in the Caledon division. They are closely related to the Thymelaeaceae.

1 **Stylapterus fruticulosus** (*L.f.*) *A. Juss.*
Derivation: Stylapterus (Greek), a style without wings; fruticosus (Latin), shrubby.
Distribution: Common in southern Cape Peninsula to Malmesbury, where it is rarer.
Leaves variable; those on basal parts of the plant larger and more elongated than those on the upper branches. Flowers July–November, but odd branches flower throughout the year.

THYMELAEACEAE
Fifty genera and 500 species found in tropical and temperate countries. Most are shrubs and they have the characteristically tough, stringy bark which was used by Hottentots and early settlers as rope.

2 **Struthiola leptantha** *Bol.*
Derivation: Strouthos (Greek), a small bird (sparrow); struthiola a Latin diminutive; leptanthus (Greek), with delicate flowers.
Distribution: Namaqualand to Worcester.
A small straggling shrub, 50 cm–1 m in height. Flowers arising in the axils of the uppermost leaves on a shoot, forming a spike-like inflorescence. The eight fleshy yellow structures at the mouth of the calyx tube are regarded as reduced petals. Flowers June–October.

3 **Gnidia pinifolia** *L.*
Derivation: A Greek name for Daphne; pini- (Latin), pine-like; folius (Latin), leaf.
Distribution: Widespread in the Cape.
A shrub, 16–40 cm tall. Calyx sepals prominent, white-pink, pubescent. Petals small and densely hairy. Eight stamens; the four upper anthers smaller than others. Flowers June–November.

4 **Gnidia geminiflora** *E. Mey.*
Derivation: Geminiflora (Latin), with flowers in pairs.
Distribution: Calvinia, Vanrhynsdorp, Ceres to Malmesbury.
Leaves hairy and opposite. Flowers always paired. Sepals with long tube and silky free portions. Four bifid petals. Eight stamens. Flowers July–December.

5 **Cryptadenia grandiflora** (*L.f.*) *Meisn.*
Derivation: Cryptos (Greek), concealed; aden (Greek), a gland; grandiflora (Latin), with large flowers.
Distribution: Caledon, Cape Peninsula to Malmesbury – frequent on the flats.
A shrub up to 30 cm tall. Calyx pink or white, covered with short silky hairs. Flowers August–November, depending on the rains, often with a few flowers throughout the year.

6 **Cryptadenia uniflora** *Meisn.*
Derivation: Uniflorus (Latin), with one flower.
Common Name: Letjiesbos.
Distribution: Clanwilliam to the Cape Peninsula.
The leaves needle-like and spine tipped. Varies in colour from white to pink. Flowers October–February.

7 **Lachnaea capitata** *Meisn.*
Derivation: Lachneeis (Greek), woolly; capitatus (Latin), with a knob-like head.
Common Name: Vleiblom.
Distribution: South western Cape to Namaqualand.
A shrub up to 50 cm tall. Young stems glabrous and reddish-brown. Outgrowths in calyx tube hair-like. Flowers July–January.

8 **Lachnaea eriocephala** *L.*
Derivation: Eriocephalus (Greek), woolly-headed.
Distribution: Sir Lowry's Pass to Malmesbury.
Leaves distinctly 4-ranked. Flowers in solitary terminal heads surrounded by involucral bracts. Calyx sepals white and densely hairy, lobes unequal. Flowers August–September.

FRANKENIACEAE
A tropical and temperate family of 4 genera and 90 species. Salt-loving herbs.

9 **Frankenia hirsuta** *L.*
Derivation: Named in honour of Johann Franke (or Frankenius), professor of anatomy and botany at Uppsala (1590–1661); hirsutus (Latin), covered with fairly coarse stiff long hairs.
Common Name: Sea Heath.
Distribution: Widespread in the Cape on damp sand and mud near the sea or vleis.
A low prostrate perennial with simple opposite exstipulate leaves. Five petals with broad blade and membranous ligule. Six stamens. Sharply 3-angled fruit. Flowers December–February.

1.

2

3

4

7

5

6

9

8

8

6

H Mason

PLATE 65

UMBELLIFERAE

Two hundred and seventy-five genera and 2 850 species – world-wide – chiefly in northern temperate areas. Stems with hollow internodes and alternate ensheathing leaves. Flowers arranged in umbel heads.

1 **Lichtensteinia beiliana** *E. & Z.*

Derivation: Genus honours a 19th-century German traveller at the Cape – H. Lichtenstein, later Director of the Zoological Museum in Berlin.

The species honours a German collector, Beil, who collected at the Cape in 1826 and whose specimens are in the Berlin Herbarium.

Distribution: Southern and south western Cape.

Stem up to 1 m tall with spreading branches. Leaves divided. Heads of flowers a compound collection of umbels. Flowers in summer.

2 **Arctopus echinatus** *L.*

Derivation: Arctos (Greek), a bear; pous (Greek), a foot; echinatus (Latin), armed with numerous straight hairs or spines.

Common Name: Platannadoring; Platdoring.

Distribution: Sandy areas from Malmesbury to Uitenhage.

A rosette plant with an underground stem and leaves lying flat on the surface of the soil. Leaves spiny, leafstalks red. Male flowers white or pink, born on elongated stalks. Female flowers yellow-green and at ground level, with spine-tipped bracts. Flowers June–August.

3 **Cnidium suffruticosum** *Cham. & Schlecht.*

Derivation: An old name for a pot plant; suffruticosus (Latin), woody at the base only.

Distribution: Widespread along the Cape and Natal coast.

Stems erect and smooth, branches longer than main stem. Leaves grey-green and twice divided. Flowers white, fruits dark red or purple. Flowers October–January.

4 **Carum** *sp.*

Probably an undescribed species of *Carum.*

MELIANTHACEAE

Two genera and 15 species, tropical and South African. The flowers are very irregular and stalks twisted through 180°.

5 **Melianthus minor** *L.*

Derivation: Meli (Greek), honey; anthos (Greek), flower; minor (Latin), smaller.

Common Name: Truitjie or Kruitjie-roer-my-nie.

Distribution: Malmesbury to Vanrhynsdorp.

A shrub. Leaves about six inches, with long narrow stipules. Leaf compound with wings between the leaflets. Flowers sub-terminal, surmounted by a cluster of dull red bracts. The four petals are dull brown or red and longer than the sepals. Flowers August–September.

CELASTRACEAE

Fifty-five genera and 850 tropical and temperate species. Trees or shrubs with simple leaves which are often leathery.

6 **Putterlickia pyracantha** *(L.) Endl.*

Derivation: Generic name honours Aloys Putterlick (1810–1845), a botanist at the Vienna Museum; pyro- (Greek), fire, fiery, red; acantha (Greek), a thorn.

Distribution: Widespread in South Africa.

A rigid shrub up to 3 m tall. Branches bearing straight spines. Leaves in tufts. Flowers cream, in clusters on slender red stalks. Flowers October–November.

3

5

4

1.

2

2 B
♀

H. Mason.

6

PLATE 66 PLUMBAGINACEAE

Ten genera and 500 species – world-wide, especially in salty areas and along the coast. Perennial herbs with simple alternate leaves.

1 **Limonium perigrinum** (*Berg.*) *R. A. Dyer*
Derivation: Leimon (Greek), a marsh; perigrinus (Latin), a stranger or wanderer.
Common Name: Papierblom.
Distribution: From just north of the Cape Peninsula to Clanwilliam.
A shrub up to 1 m tall. Branches leafy at the tips. Leaves simple, tapering and clasping the stem at the base with one to three visible veins when dry. Flowers in summer.

2 **Limonium equisetinum** (*Bois.*) *R. A. Dyer*
Derivation: Equus (Latin), a horse; seta (Latin), a hair – the leaves resemble horse tail hairs.
Common Name: Sea Lavender.
Distribution: Common in damp low-lying areas near the sea.
A plant with a woody branching underground stem. Leaves all basal which wither when plant flowers. Calyx hairy. Flowers December–March.

3 **Limonium capense** (*L. Bol.*) *L. Bol.*
Derivation: Capensis (Latin), of the Cape.
Common Name: Statice.
Distribution: Found only in the low coastal bush in the Hopefield district.
Shrub up to 45 cm tall; freely branched and very leafy. Leaves minutely pitted. Flowers November–December.

4 **Limonium purpuratum** (*L.*) *Hubbard ex L. H. Bailey*
Derivation: Purpuratus (Latin), dressed in purple.
Distribution: Found only from the Cape Peninsula to Malmesbury.
Plant branched, becoming woody. Leaves not very dense, three-nerved. Flower stalk much longer than the leaves. Flowers December–February.

Langebaan lagoon from Konstabel Hill

1.

2.

3.

4.

PLATE 67 ERICACEAE

Family of 50 genera and about 2 000 species with world-wide distribution. Sub family Ericoideae almost entirely confined to Africa and characterised by narrow leaves and anthers which shed their pollen through apical pores.

1 Erica ferrea *Berg.*
Derivation: Ereice (Greek). This name was used for heaths by Pliny and Theophrastus; derived from ericein (Greek), pound – referring to the supposed property of some species to break gall stones; ferreus (Latin), iron, rusty.
Distribution: Rather rare on the sandy flats in the south western Cape.
An erect, glabrous shrub up to 1 m tall with few branches. The flowers are globose, urn-shaped and rather sticky. Included anthers. Flowers December–February.

2 Erica mammosa *L.*
Derivation: Mammosus (Latin), with breasts – referring to the shape of the flowers!
Distribution: South western Cape.
The corolla is long, glabrous and tubular with four dents at the base. Near the mouth the tube narrows. Colour varies from dark red, pink to creamy white. Flowers December–April.

3 Erica plukeneti *L.*
Derivation: Named after Leonard Plukenet (1642–1706), Queen's botanist to Mary II and supervisor of Hampton Court garden. Plukenet was the first to mention Cape Heaths in 1700 in his "Almagesti Mantissa Botanici".
Distribution: Namaqualand, south western Cape to Mossel Bay and the Karoo.
A well known and common *Erica*, easily recognised because of its long inflated corolla tube with long exerted anthers. Flower colour ranges from red, orange to yellow and dirty white. Flowers March–September.

4 Erica capitata *L.*
Derivation: Capitus (Latin), a head, referring to the densely clustered flowers.
Distribution: Cape Peninsula and south western coast on sandy flats – becoming rare.
Leaves and peduncles woolly. The sepals large, conspicuous and white, or the same colour as the petals; they are densely hairy and the hairs are green turning yellow. Included stamens. Flowers October–February.

5 Erica subdivaricata *Berg.*
Derivation: Subdivaricatus (Latin), somewhat spreading.
Distribution: Common in the south western and southern Cape.
Stamens included; the corolla less than 1,4 cm long. Sepals small and inconspicuous. Anthers awned. Flowers January–May.

6 Erica pulchella *Houtt.*
Derivation: Pulchellus (Latin), beautiful.
Distribution: From the sandveld, eastwards to Albertinia.
A compact shrub, usually covered with colourful flowers. Stamens included. Flowers August–December.

7 Erica decora *Andr.*
Derivation: Decorus (Latin), pretty.
Distribution: Cape Peninsula, Stellenbosch to Malmesbury.
An elegant large-flowered *Erica*. Many plants have a few flowers on throughout the year. In moister areas, however, they flower in greater profusion.

8 Erica paniculata *L.*
Derivation: Paniculatus (Latin), paniculate, referring to the arrangement of the flowers.
Distribution: Malmesbury, Stellenbosch and Wolseley.
Flowers April–September.

9 Salaxis axillaris (*Thunb.*) *Salisb. ex G. Don.*
Derivation: Generic name unexplained by the author; axilla (Latin), armpit or having an angle.
Distribution: Sandy flats in south western and southern Cape.
A small, erect shrub with inconspicuous flowers, their colour derived from the red-brown anthers. Flowers at various times during the year.

10 Grisebachia incana *Klotzsch*
Derivation: Named in honour of Heinrich Rudolf August Grisebach, who held the Chair of systematic botany and plant geography in Berlin (1843–1853) and Professor of botany at Göttingen; incanus (Latin), hoary, white.
Distribution: South western Cape.
A fairly hairy plant with terminal clusters of small pink flowers with an exserted style and spurred anthers. There are four stamens whereas *Erica* has eight. Flowers April–June.

1

2A

2B

3

4

10

6

5

8

7

9

H Mason.

PLATE 68

EBENACEAE
A family of 7 genera and 320 species, mainly tropical. Usually trees or shrubs with entire leaves. Many of these trees yield valuable woods.

1 **Euclea racemosa** *Murr.*
Derivation: Eucleia (Greek), glory, alluding to the evergreen foliage; racemus (Latin), a bunch or cluster.
Common Name: Kersbos.
Distribution: A coastal dune shrub, also found in coastal forests. Endemic in the Cape Province from Namaqualand to Bathurst.
Bark grey and smooth, branchlets often reddish. Flowers sweet scented. Fruits at first red then black, the pulp is sweet and eaten by birds. Flowers April–June.

ASCLEPIADACEAE
Two hundred and ten genera and about 1 700 species, mostly tropical but some temperate. These plants frequently have a milky latex especially the non-succulents. The flower structure is very complicated. As a pollination adaptation the pollen grains are often joined into waxy masses which are transported in various ways by visiting pollinators.
The fruit is characteristically a large V-shaped pod that splits open along one side. The seeds have tufts of hairs which facilitate distribution by wind.

2 **Asclepias crispa** *Berg.*
Derivation: Name honours Asclepios, mythical god of medicine; crispus (Latin), irregularly waved, kinky, curled.
Common Name: Bitterwortel (this name is used in other parts of South Africa but not known in Darling).
Distribution: Widespread in the Cape.
A herb 20–30 cm high, with a branched pubescent stem. Leaves hairy with crisped margins. Flowers very complicated. Flowers November–May.

3 **Cynanchum obtusifolium** *L.f.*
Derivation: Cyno- (Greek), dog; agchein (Greek), to kill or strangle – referring to the poisonous properties of some species; obtusus (Latin), blunt; folium (Latin), a leaf.
Common Name: Klimop, Opklim.
Distribution: Widespread along the whole coast up to Natal.
A climber which reaches the tops of the coastal bushes. Leaves are broadly rounded or cordate at the base and poisonous. Fragrant. Flowers throughout the year.

4 **Microloma sagittatum** *R. Br.*
Derivation: Micros (Greek), small; loma (Greek), a fringe – referring to the fringe of hairs in the corolla tube; sagittatus (Latin), shaped like an arrowhead.
Common Name: Wax creeper; Suikerkannetjie. In Darling it is known as Bokmaellie.
Distribution: Widespread throughout the Cape Province.
A slender climber with leaves pubescent on both sides. These are tuberous and fleshy; the aerial shoot is shed in summer. Corolla pink and tubular. The flowers contain much nectar. Nectar from the flowers is sought after. Flowers July–September.

OLEACEAE
Twenty-one genera and 400 species; tropical and temperate. Shrubs and trees usually with opposite leaves. Valuable woods are obtained from the olive and ash. Popular garden shrubs are the lilac and privet.

5 **Olea africana** *Mill.*
Derivation: Oleum (Latin), oil; africanus (Latin), of Africa.
Common Name: Wild olive.
Distribution: Widespread throughout Africa.
A small rounded tree or shrub up to 10 m tall. Olive wood is very dense, hard and heavy. The fruits exude an oily substance when crushed. (Olive oil from *Olea europaea*.) The fruits of this species are edible but so small they are not commercially economical. Flowers November–December.

1.

2

2

2

1.

3

H. mason.

4

5

PLATE 69

GENTIANACEAE

Eighty genera and 900 species – found all over the world from the arctic to salty marshes. Plants usually herbaceous and sometimes perennial. Eight genera are found in the Republic.

1 **Orphium frutescens** *E. Mey.*
Derivation: An allusion to Orpheus, the Greek mythical character; frutescens (Latin), becoming shrubby.
Common Name: Teeringbos.
Distribution: Common on sandy flats near the coast in south western Cape.
A shrub, usually pubescent. As illustrated, the leaves can vary from broad to narrow. A conspicuous glandular disc at the base of the corolla tube separates it from the calyx. Corolla lobes twisted in the bud, later spreading. The five stamens lie to one side of the stigma. The anthers shed their pollen through an apical pore and twist immediately afterwards. Flowers November–February.

2 **Chironia baccifera** *L.*
Derivation: Chiron (Greek), a centaur and father of medicine, surgery and botany; baccifer (Latin), berry-bearing.
Common Name: Toothache berry; Christmas berry; Gentian; Perdebossie; Bitterbos.
Distribution: Dunes and dry sandy soil from Namaqualand to Natal.
A bushy plant, 1 m tall. Flowers pink, up to 1,5 cm across. Calyx keeled and glabrous. Fruit a red berry (only species with a berry). This plant grows easily from seed and makes a good garden subject. Widely differing medicinal properties are attributed to this plant. Flowers intermittently.

3 **Chironia linoides** *L.*
Derivation: Like *Linum* – the flax.
Distribution: Endemic in the Cape Province.
Leaves narrowly linear. Flowers up to 2 cm long, corolla lobes obviously longer than broad. Found usually in moist places. Flowers November–January.

4 **Sebaea aurea** *(L. f.) R. & S.*
Derivation: Named after Albert Seba (1665–1736), an apothecary and naturalist of Amsterdam; aureus (Latin), golden yellow.
Distribution: Endemic in the winter rainfall area of the south western Cape.
An annual. Leaves opposite. Flowers white or yellow. Four petals. Calyx lobes (sepals) with wing-like keel. Mature anthers longer than filament. Flowers October–December.

5 **Sebaea exacoides** *Schinz*
Derivation: Like *Exacum*, a genus of the same family.
Distribution: Endemic in the south western Cape.
An annual 5–30 cm tall. Five petals and sepals. Calyx lobes winged and strongly veined. Style with stigmatic swelling and anthers with glands at their apex. Flowers August–October.

EBENACEAE

6 **Diospyros austro-africana** *de Winter*
var. **rugosa** *(E. Mey ex A.DC.) de Winter (=Royena hirsuta var. rugosa).*
Derivation: Dios (Greek), divine; pyros (Greek), wheat, a grain – referring to the edible fruit; australis (Latin), southern; africanus (Latin), Africa; rugosus (Latin), wrinkled.
Distribution: Widespread in the Republic. This variety is found from Malmesbury to Clanwilliam.
This plant belongs to the family Ebenaceae illustrated on Plate 68. Shrubs are up to 3 m tall. Leaves up to 3,5 cm long, upper surface glossy and margins revolute. Flowers in September.

1.

2.

3.

3.

4.

5.

6.

H. mason.

PLATE 70

CONVOLVULACEAE

A tropical and temperate family of 55 genera and 1 600 species. Many are climbers with tuberous roots, often with latex in the stems. The flowers are usually large and showy and other than *Ipompoea batatas* (the sweet potato) they are of little economic importance.

1 **Convolvulus capensis** *Burm. f.*
Derivation: Convolvere (Latin), to entwine; capensis (Latin), of the Cape.
Distribution: Calvinia to Bredasdorp.
A twiner with long stems. Leaves hairy and lobed. Flowers May–September.

BORAGINACEAE

A family of 100 genera and 2 000 species. Tropical and temperate with a focal point in the Mediterranean countries. The inflorescence is usually a very characteristic coiled cyme (cf. the Forget-me-not). The ovary is of four separate parts which form separate nutlets when ripe.

2 **Lobostemon fruticosus** *(L.) Buek*
Derivation: Lobos (Greek), a lobe; stemon (Greek), a thread; fruticosus (Latin), shrubby.
Common Name: Luibossie.
Distribution: Western and south western Cape.
A branched shrub up to 1 m high. Flowers blue or pink, very rarely white. Flowers August–November.

3 **Lobostemon glaucophyllus** *(Jacq.) Buek*
Derivation: Glaucophyllus (Latin), with grey-green leaves.
Distribution: From the Cape Peninsula to Little Namaqualand.
A branched shrub up to 1 m tall. Leaves with adpressed hairs often giving them a silvery appearance. Flowers July–November.

4 **Lobostemon hispidus** *DC.*
Derivation: Hispidus (Latin), bristly.
Distribution: Widespread in the western Cape.
Small shrub to 1 m. Common on gravelly or heavy clay soils. Flowers blue, occasionally white or pink. Flowers July–October.

5 **Echiostachys incanus** *(Thunb.) Levyns*
Derivation: Echium – a genus of the Boraginaceae, stachys (Greek), a spike, i.e. a spike like Echium; incanus (Latin), hoary.
Distribution: South western Cape.
A tuberous rooted perennial herb with a rosette of linear pubescent leaves. Inflorescences dense, elongated. Flowers cream, stamens exerted. Flowers September–October.

VERBENACEAE

Seventy-five genera and 3 000 species, almost all tropical and subtropical.
Lantana camara is a proclaimed noxious weed in the Republic. *Tectona grandis* from Indomalaya produces the wood teak. The leaves of *Lippia citriodora* produce the aromatic verbena oil; 17 genera are found in South Africa and 4 are endemic to the south western Cape.

6 **Stilbe ericoides** *L.*
Derivation: Stilbe (Greek), mirror, lamp; ericoides (Greek), like an *Erica*.
Distribution: Confined to the sandy flats along the coastal belt from Malmesbury to Bredasdorp.
A small shrub up to 50 cm tall. Slender stems covered with overlapping ericoid leaves. Flowers arranged in ovoid spikes. Petals pale pink to bright magenta. Flowers June–December.

SELAGINACEAE

A small family allied to Scrophulariaceae but distinguished by having a single ovule in each of the two chambers of the ovary. The Selaginaceae is confined to Africa and Madagascar.

7 **Selago tenuis** *E. Mey.*
Derivation: An ancient name for the club moss, the small leaves give members of this genus a superficial resemblance to the club moss; tenuis (Latin), thin, fine.
Distribution: Little Karoo to Sandveld.
A perennial with five calyx lobes and four stamens. Flowers September–October.

8 **Hebenstreitia dentata** *L.*
Derivation: Named in honour of J. E. Hebenstreit, a professor at Leipzig; dentatus (Latin), toothed.
Distribution: Widespread in the Cape Province and into Natal.
Calyx bract-like, four well-developed petals with a rudimentary one lower down the tube. Common. Flowers June–December.

1

2

3

4

5

6

7

8

H mason

PLATE 71 LABIATAE

The Salvia family has 200 genera and 3 000 species. World-wide, especially Mediterranean. Most are herbs and undershrubs. The stem is usually square with pairs of leaves opposite in arrangement on stem. Many have a characteristic smell caused by the volatile oils secreted by epidermal glands. The flowers are two-lipped with a complicated hinged stamen arrangement. Well known plants belonging to this family are rosemary, thyme and lavender.

1 Stachys aethiopica L.

Derivation: Stachys (Greek), ear of corn, spike; aethiopia (Latin), Africa, usually South Africa.
Common Name: Kattekruie.
Distribution: Frequent on hilly slopes throughout the Cape Province.
A perennial herb 20–40 cm in height. Amongst African tribes, this plant is said to be effective against snake-bite. A few flowers throughout the year with the peak in May–December.

2 Salvia nivea *Thunb.*

Derivation: Salvere (Latin), to be in good health, alluding to the medicinal properties claimed for many members of the genus or family; niveus (Latin), snowy.
Distribution: Commonly found from Vanrhynsdorp to the Peninsula.
A shrub up to 1 m in height. Leaves with a grey tomentum. Inflorescence bracts deciduous and flowers brownish-crimson. Flowers November–March.

3 Salvia africana – lutea L.

Derivation: Africanus (Latin), of Africa; luteus (Latin), deep yellow.
Common Name: Geelsalie, Sandsalie, Geel medisyn.
Distribution: Common on coastal sand from Namaqualand to Port Elizabeth.
Bracts at the base of the flower persistent; flowers rusty brown. Flowers 3 cm long or more. Flowers June–December.

4 Salvia africana – coerulea L.

Derivation: Africanus (Latin), of Africa; coerulus (Latin), blue.
Common Name: Blousalie, Blou medisyn.
Distribution: South western Cape.
Flowers less than 2,5 cm long. An infusion of this plant is commonly used to relieve colds. Calyx enlarges in fruit. Flowers August–December.

5 Leonotus leonurus R. Br.

Derivation: Leon (Greek), a lion; ous (Greek), an ear – referring to the shape of the hairy flower.
Common Name: Wild dagga. The leaf of this plant closely resembles that of Indian hemp – *Cannabis sativa* – but has none of its narcotic properties.
Distribution: Frequent throughout the Cape Province, eastern Transvaal and Natal.
Plants up to 2 m tall. Flowers densely clustered in distinct whorls in the axils of upper leaves. Corolla two-lipped, upper lip very elongated, concave and densely hairy. Lower lip petals wither very soon. Petals are white while the dense hairs are filled with an orange cell sap giving the flower an orange coloration. Frequently visited by the colourful sun-birds. Flowers November–January.

6 Ballota africana *Benth.*

Derivation: Ballota – a Latinised form of the Greek name used for this genus by Dioscorides; africanus (Latin), of Africa.
Common Name: Kattekruie.
Distribution: Widespread in Cape Province.
An erect woody perennial. Leaves covered with minute gland-tipped hairs. Flowers in spring.

1.

2

3

4

5

6

H mason

PLATE 72 SOLANACEAE

Seventy-two genera and 3 000 species tropical and temperate in distribution, chiefly central and south America. Economically important are *Solanum* (potato), *Nicotiana* (tobacco) and *Lycopersicum* (tomato). Many favourite garden plants also belong to this family, e.g. *Petunia*, *Schizanthus*, *Nierembergia*. Eight genera are found in the Republic.

1 **Lycium afrum** *L.*
Derivation: It comes from Lycia, a province in Asia Minor. (S.W. Turkey.)
Common Name: Kaffir Thorn, Bokdoring.
Distribution: South western Cape to Namaqualand.
A spiny, woody shrub. Leaves are narrow and grouped in dense clusters at the nodes or base of spines. Petals fused to form a longish tube. Stamens more or less equal in length and the filaments have globose tufts of hairs. Fruit a fleshy black berry. Flowers November–May.

2 **Lycium ferocissimum** *Miers*
Derivation: Ferocissimus (Latin), the very spiniest.
Distribution: Widespread in the Cape.
A glabrous, leafy, straggling shrub up to 1,5 m, branches ending in short spines. Flowers campanulate in shape with exerted stamens. Fruit red and spherical. Flowers in May–November.

2A **Lycium sp. indet.**
Distribution: Coastal belt from Saldanha Bay to Vredendal.
A glabrous, spiny shrub to 2 m in height. It has been confused with *L. ferocissimum* in some herbaria, but its identity is uncertain. This species is probably undescribed. Flowers in July.

3 **Solanum tomentosum** *L.*
Derivation: Solanum is the Latin name for Nightshade (that deadly plant is a member of this genus); tomentosus (Latin), thickly covered with short matted hairs.
Common Name: Bitterappel, Gifappel.
Distribution: Clanwilliam to eastern Cape.
A straggling spinous shrub up to 1,5 m high. Young stems and leaves covered with yellow-brown stellate hairs. Leaves densely hairy on both surfaces. Fruit is less than 1,5 cm in diameter. Flowers September–October.

4 **Solanum sodomaeum** *L.* var. **hermanii** *Dun.*
Derivation: Sodomaeus (Latin), of Sodom. The apple of Sodom is a mythical fruit, externally beautiful, but when one grasped it, it turned to smoke and ashes. Generally it refers to anything hollow and disappointing. A good description of the fruit of this plant. The variety honours Paul Hermann, professor of botany at Leiden (1640–1695).
Common Name: Bitterappel, Gifappel.
Distribution: A common roadside weed in south western and eastern Cape.
Young stems purple and hairy. Spines straight and the numerous leaves deeply lobed. Flowers July–December.

5 **Solanum guineense** *L.*
Derivation: Guineense (Latin), belonging to Guinea. Linnaeus erroneously thought the plant came from Guinea.
Common Name: Melkellie.
Distribution: Widespread in the Cape Province.
Plants which grow in deep shade do not flower. Plants glabrous with practically no spines. Fruit globose and yellow. Flowering season irregular.

1.

3

3

1

2 A

2

H Mason

5

4

PLATE 73 SCROPHULARIACEAE

Two hundred genera and 2 600 species found the world over. Most are herbs and small shrubs although a few are trees. The flowers are usually markedly irregular and pollinated by insects. Many favourite garden flowers like Antirrhinum and Pentstemon belong to this family.

1 **Manulea cheiranthus** L.
Derivation: Manus (Latin), a hand; cheir (Greek), a hand; anthos (Greek), a flower.
Distribution: From Namaqualand along the coastal regions to Plettenberg Bay.
An annual, 3–40 cm tall, minutely hairy with long narrow tapering corolla lobes, the margins curling back slightly. Corolla very irregular. Flowers July–February.

2 **Manulea tomentosa** L.
Derivation: Tomentosus (Latin), thickly or evenly covered with hair.
Distribution: Cape Peninsula to Mamre.
Commonly found on low lying areas near the sea. Leaves densely hairy and the branches often creeping. Corolla lobes very obtuse. Flowers July–December.

3 **Manulea rubra** L. f.
Derivation: Ruber (Latin), red.
Distribution: South western Cape.
Calyx deeply five-lobed. Stem leafy all the way up and leaves often incised. Flowers throughout the year.

4 **Manulea altissima** L. f.
Derivation: Altissimus (Latin), the tallest.
Distribution: Found in sandy areas from Windhoek in South West Africa through Namaqualand to the Sandveld.
An erect herb, usually perennial and woody at the base. Corolla two-lipped. Flowers August–October.

5 **Manulea benthamiana** *Hiern*
Derivation: Named in honour of George Bentham, F.R.S. (1800–1884), a distinguished British botanist who worked in collaboration with J. D. Hooker of Kew to devise a system of classification of higher plants.
Distribution: Found along the south western coastal region from Vanrhynsdorp to Cape Flats and through to the Bathurst district in the eastern Cape Province.
An herbaceous annual. Flowers arranged in clustered terminal head. Calyx deeply five-lobed, regular. Throat of corolla hairy. Flowers September–October.

6 **Harveya squamosa** (*Thunb.*) *Steud.*
Derivation: Named in honour of W. H. Harvey, a British botanist who spent the years 1840–1844 at the Cape as Colonial Treasurer. (He first came out here in 1835 for a short while.) He wrote the first "Genera of South African Plants" as well as the "Flora Capensis" (with Sonder); squama (Latin), scale.
Common Name: Jakkalskos.
Distribution: From Namaqualand through Swartland and Sandveld. Rare on the Cape Peninsula but recorded from Natal.
Parasitic with no green leaves. Flowers turning brown. Style bent at the junction with the tongue-like stigma. Flowers October–December.

7 & 7B **Polycarena capensis** *Benth.*
Derivation: Poly- (Greek), many; carenon (Greek), heads.
Distribution: From Sandveld to Milnerton.
A slightly sticky hairy annual. Corolla regular, the tube 15 mm long. Four stamens, two extending outside corolla tube. Flowers September–October.

8 **Polycarena selaginoides** *Schlt.*
Derivation: Like a *Selago*, a large genus of the family Selaginaceae.
Distribution: Vanrhynsdorp to Darling.
A slightly hairy annual. Corolla tube longer than the calyx. Flowers September–October.

9 **Sutera tristis** (*L. f.*) *Hiern*
Derivation: Named in honour of J. R. Suter, professor of botany at Berne; tristis (Latin), sad, dull coloured.
Distribution: Frequent on sandy flats. Through Namaqualand, Sandveld and Little Karoo.
An annual. Flowers almost regular, both calyx and corolla. Flowers very sweetly scented at night. Flowers September—December.

168

H mason.

PLATE 74 SCROPHULARIACEAE

1 **Nemesia barbata** *Benth.*
Derivation: From an old name used by the Greek, Dioscorides, for a similar plant; barbatus (Latin), bearded.
Common Name: Kappie, Oumakappie, Weeskindertjie.
Distribution: South western Cape.
An annual. Corolla two-lipped, the lower lip always a deep velvety blue and white at the base. Flowers August–September.

2 **Nemesia versicolor** *E. Mey. ex Benth.*
Derivation: Versicolor (Latin), variously coloured or changing colour.
Common Name: Weeskindertjies.
Distribution: Common in sandy areas from southern Namaqualand to Knysna.
An annual. Corolla two-lipped, the lower lip with a short spine or pouch. Flowers blue, mauve, yellow or white with two lips of differing colours, or reverse of flower a different colour. Flowers June–November, but greatly influenced by the rainfall.

3 **Nemesia strumosa** *Benth.*
Derivation: Strumosus (Latin), provided with a swelling.
Common Name: Nemesia, in Darling known as Balsa mienie.
Distribution: Confined to the Sandveld.
An annual. Corolla has a broad pouch or pocket rather than a spur. Flowers large, pink, lilac, reddish, orange and white. Seeds of this plant were collected on the beautiful family coastal farm "Bokbaai". In 1891 they were sent by Hildagonda Duckitt (of cooking fame and author of "Hilda's where is it") to Suttons, the seed merchants in England, from whence the seeds have been distributed all over the world. This species and its cultivars are now one of the most popular garden plants the world over. Flowers September–October.

4 **Nemesia bicornis** *Pers.*
Derivation: Bi- (Latin), two; cornis (Latin), horned.
Common Name: Kaapse leeubekkie.
Distribution: Namaqualand to Cape Peninsula.
An annual. Spur as long as the lower lip. Fruit widest at the top and not warted. Flowers July–October.

5 **Linaria arvensis** *Desf.*
Derivation: Linum (Latin), flax; arvum (Latin), a cultivated field.
Introduced from Europe and now very widespread. Flowers in September.

6 **Hemimeris sabulosa** *L. f.*
Derivation: Hemi- (Greek), half; meros (Greek), a part; sabulosus (Latin), growing in sandy places.
Distribution: Common on sandy flats throughout western and south western Cape.
This genus is endemic in South Africa and there are nine described species. A herbaceous annual with solitary yellow flowers and corolla with two small pouches. Flowers August–October.

7 **Zaluzianskya villosa** *F. W. Schmidt*
Derivation: Named in honour of Adam Zaluziansky, a physician from Prague (1558–1613); villosus (Latin), shaggy with fairly long, straight hair.
Distribution: Common on sandy patches in south western and southern Cape.
A densely hairy annual. Corolla regular, white or mauve with a yellow eye. Corolla lobes bifid. Fragrant at night. Flowers June–October.

8 **Diascia diffusa** *Benth.*
Derivation: Di (Greek), two; askion (Greek), a small bladder; diffusus (Latin), loosely irregular.
Distribution: Clanwilliam to Caledon.
Two small pouches on the corolla. Four stamens, the filaments divided. Flowers July–October.

1.

L

1.

2

2

2

3

7

2

5

3

4

4

6

8

H mason   4

PLATE 75

SCROPHULARIACEAE

1 **Sutera linifolia** *O. Kuntze*

Derivation: Named in honour of J. R. Suter, professor of botany at Berne; linifolius (Latin), flax-like leaf.

Distribution: Widespread.

An erect branched plant up to 50 cm. Woody below. Leaves usually entire but sometimes slightly toothed. Corolla tube often slightly curved, flowers blue and mauve. Flowers May–September.

2 **Hyobanche sanguinea** *L.*

Derivation: Hys (Greek), a pig; agchein (Greek), to strangle; sanguineus (Latin), blood red.

Distribution: Widespread in the Cape.

A parasite growing on the roots of a variety of hosts. Inflorescence up to 15 cm high. Petals fused, bright pink and shaggy outside. Flowers July–October.

DIPSACACEAE

Eight genera and 150 species – chiefly north temperate, tropical and South African. Flowers arranged in dense heads, the outer flowers of the head have longer petals on the outer side.

3 **Scabiosa incisa** *Mill.*

Derivation: Members of this genus are used to cure itch and scabies – hence the name; incisus (Latin), incised, divided.

Distribution: Mamre, coastal farms especially Bokkerivier.

This large and beautiful *Scabiosa* is found in a very restricted area along the coast, from Buck Bay to Piketberg. Flowers in spring and early summer.

CUCURBITACEAE

One hundred and ten genera and 640 species, abundant in the tropics but not found in cold regions. Mainly climbing herbs with tendrils. Many of the members of this family have edible fruits, viz. pumpkins, marrows, watermelon and cucumber. In South Africa we find 16 genera and 65 species. Cucurbitacean fruits are often poisonous, particularly when they have a bitter taste.

4 **Kedrostis nana** *(Lam.) Cogn.*

Derivation: Kedrostis, a Greek name for bryony (a European member of the Cucurbitaceae); nanus (Latin), dwarf.

Distribution: Widespread.

This plant belongs to a complex and variable group which have not been intensively collected and consequently are not well known. The flowers shown here are male. Flowers intermittently.

PLATE 76 CAMPANULACEAE

Sixty–seventy genera and 2 000 species, temperate and tropical; most are perennial herbs often with latex. Nectar is secreted in the flower by the disc which is usually covered by the flattened bases of the stamens, thus only allowing an insect proboscis to penetrate. Flowers are usually blue and probably all are pollinated by bees. Many species of the genera *Campanula* and *Lobelia* are favourite garden subjects.

1 Cyphia digitata *Willd.*
Derivation: Cyphos (Greek), curved; digitatus (Latin), having fingers.
Common Name: Witbokkies, Rooistormbos.
Distribution: South western and southern coastal regions.
A twiner. Mature older leaves palmately lobed (like a hand) as reflected in the species name. Flowers August–October.

2 Cyphia bulbosa *Berg.*
Derivation: Bulbosus (Latin), bulbous.
Common Name: Barroe, Melkbarroe.
Distribution: South western Cape.
A bulbous-rooted plant with erect woody stems and lobed leaves decreasing in size from the base upwards. Flowers most freely in August and September, especially after fires.

3A Wahlenbergia sp.
Distribution: Malmesbury.
Flowers in January.

3B Wahlenbergia paniculata *A. DC.*
Derivation: Named in honour of G. Wahlenberg, a Swedish botanist.
Distribution: Piketberg, Malmesbury, Clanwilliam, Worcester and Langebaan.
Flowers bell-shaped, filaments broad and stigmas terminal. Ovary partly inferior. Flowers in summer.

4 Wahlenbergia capensis *(L.) A. DC.*
Derivation: Capensis (Latin), of the Cape.
Distribution: Cape Flats, Sandveld and Tulbagh.
Flowers terminal and solitary. Ovary five-chambered and densely hairy. Flowers October–December.

5 Monopsis simplex *(L.) E. Wimmer*
Derivation: Monos (Greek), one; opsis (Greek), a face; simplex (Latin), simple, undivided.
Distribution: South western Cape.
Corolla tube cleft down one side to the base. Anthers all bearded. Flowers in October.

6 Monopsis lutea *(L.) Urb.*
Derivation: Luteus (Latin), deep yellow.
Distribution: Riversdale along the coast to Vanrhynsdorp.
Corolla cleft, three petals in upper lip and two in lower. Anthers all bearded. Flowers November–April.

7 Microcodon glomeratum *A. DC.*
Derivation: Micros (Greek), small; odon (Greek), tooth; glomeratus (Latin), collected closely together into a head.
Distribution: Sandveld–Tulbagh.
Flowers sessile and in heads. Four stamens. Bracts joined to the base of the calyx. Flowers October–December.

8 Roella arenaria *Schlt.*
Derivation: Named in honour of G. Roelle, a Dutch anatomist; arenarius (Latin), growing on sand.
Distribution: Bredasdorp along coast to Darling.
Flowers solitary, ovary and calyx hairy. Bracts crowded and toothed. Flowers November–January.

1.

1.

2.

3 B

5

7

8

3 A

4

6

H Mason.

PLATE 77 CAMPANULACEAE

1 Lobelia coronopifolia L.
Derivation: Named in honour of M. de L'Obel, a sixteenth century Dutch botanist; coronopifolia (Latin), with leaves like *Coronopus*, the crowfoot.
Distribution: Widespread.
All anthers with tufts of hair on the tips. Corolla tubes 3–4 cm long. Flowers at intervals throughout the year, especially November–March.

2 Lobelia setacea *Thunb.*
Derivation: Setaceus (Latin), bristle-like.
Distribution: South western Cape.
Leaves simple, narrow and widely scattered. Flower stalk shorter than, or as long as, the bract. Flowers November–April.

3 Lobelia alata *Labill.* var. minor *(Sond.)* E. Wimmer
Derivation: Alatus (Latin), winged – referring to the stems.
Distribution: South western Cape.
Prostrate, rooting at the nodes. Stems winged, leaves entire but toothed. Common in marshes and vleis. Flowers December–June.

4 Lobelia comosa L.
Derivation: Comosus (Latin), bearing a tuft of hairs or leaves.
Distribution: South western Cape.
Erect, the stems ridged and woody at the base. Most of the leaves clustered at the base of the 50 cm tall plants. Older leaves purple. Flowers usually blue, sometimes pale pink. Flowers November–May.

5 Prismatocarpus fruticosus *L'Herit.*
Derivation: Prisma (Greek), a prism; karpos (Greek), a fruit; fruticosus (Latin), shrubby; bushy.
Distribution: South western Cape.
Ovary very narrow, stalk-like and completely inferior. Fruit splitting into five strips. Flowers in summer.

Pteronia in fruit and thornbushes at Langebaan

1.

2

3

4

5

H Mason

PLATE 78 COMPOSITAE

One of the largest families of flowering plants with 900 genera and more than 13 000 species – about 10% of the world's total. Plants of this family have a world-wide distribution (marsh plants and climbers are rare). The members of this family tend to be xerophytic in their adaptations.

The flowers are all arranged in distinct heads or capitulae. The heads are surrounded by an involucre of bracts arranged in one or more rows. The capitulum of flowers is arranged on the apex of the flowering stem. Generally there are flowers of two different shapes in the head. The ray florets which resemble petals are towards the outside. These flowers have their petals all fused to form a strap; they can be sterile, unisexual or bisexual. The central flowers are called disc florets. These are regular in shape with petals fused to form a long tube with short free tips. The disc florets are usually bisexual. Some capitulae contain only ray florets – some only disc – but more commonly both.

1 **Arctotis hirsuta** *(Harv.) Lewin*
Derivation: Arctos (Greek), a bear; ous (Greek), an ear; hirsutus (Latin), hairy with coarse and stiff long hairs.
Common Name: Gousblom.
Distribution: South western Cape.
Leaves with long, jointed hairs. Basal leaves lobed, the upper ones small and entire. Involucral bracts bristly with reflexed tips. Rays orange and the disc florets dark. Flowers September–December.

2 **Arctotis breviscapa** *Thunb.*
Derivation: Brevi- (Latin), short; scap- (Latin), relating to the scape, a leafless peduncle or floral axis arising from the rootstock.
Common Name: Gousblom.
Distribution: South western Cape.
An annual with pinnately lobed basal leaves with scattered hairs on the upper surface and white and woolly below. Outer involucral bracts acute with reflexed tips; inner ones obtuse. Corolla of the ray florets orange-yellow with paler underside. Flowers August–January.

3 **Arctotis revoluta** *Jacq.*
Derivation: Revolutus (Latin), rolled back from the edge.
Distribution: On sandy coastal areas from Saldanha Bay to Breede River.
A perennial which roots at the nodes. Leaves pinnately lobed with very wavy margins. Flowers bright yellow. Flowers August–November.

4 **Felicia bergerana** *(Sprengel) O. Hoffm.*
Derivation: Named after a German official, Felix; species honours Ernst Berger, a German botanist who died in 1853.
Distribution: South western Cape.
An annual covered with weak hairs. Capitula solitary. Leaves entire or slightly toothed. Flowers August–October.

5 **Felicia tenella** *(L.) Nees*
Derivation: Tenellus (Latin), delicate.
Common Name: Cineraria.
Distribution: South western and western Cape.
A small plant with narrow linear leaves that are rigidly ciliate. Peduncle bearing a solitary flower that has several rows of involucral bracts, the innermost longer than the outer. Rays white·to lilac. Flowers mainly September–February.

6 **Amellus asteroides** *(L.) Druce*
Derivation: An old name used by Virgil; asteroides (Greek), like a star.
Distribution: Caledon to Piketberg.
The plants from Caledon to the Cape Peninsula have much broader leaves than those up the West Coast. Most of the plant densely covered with short hairs. Ligulate flowers lilac to white. Painting shows old dead flower heads. Flowers October–March.

H Mason

PLATE 79 COMPOSITAE

1 **Eriocephalus africanus** *L.*
Derivation: Erion (Greek), wool; cephale (Greek), head.
Common Name: Kapokbossie, Wilde-roosmaryn (in Darling district only).
Distribution: Widespread in the Cape.
A branched shrub up to 1 m. Leaves simple or divided and often silvery in appearance. Usually 3 but up to 5 ray florets. Capitulum in fruit has a densely woolly appearance. Flowers May–September.

2 **Othonna cylindrica** *DC.*
Derivation: Othone (Greek), a linen cloth or napkin (alluding to a downy covering of some of the species which were first described); cylindrica (Latin), cylindrical.
Distribution: Sandveld to Clanwilliam, common along the Olifants River.
A loosely branched shrub. Leaves fleshy, green-grey in colour, tapering at the base and spreading; 8–9 involucral bracts, free nearly to the base. Flowers June–July.

3 **Othonna filicaulis** *Jacq.*
Derivation: Filium (Latin), a thread; caulis (Latin), a stem (a thread-like stem).
Distribution: Namaqualand to George.
Cultivated in Europe in 19th century. Root tuberous. Radical leaves stalked but the leaves on the stem heart-shaped or cordate, clasping the stem. 10–12 involucral bracts. The hairs at the base of the minute florets in the heads are reddish-purple. Flowers June–August.

3A Colour variant of **Othonna filicaulis.**

4 **Othonna arborescens** *L.*
Derivation: Arborescens (Latin), becoming tree-like.
Distribution: South western Cape.
A small shrub with succulent stem, becoming woody. 5 involucral bracts in a single row, glabrous, forming a smooth cup at the base; alternate bracts with hard, toothed margin. Flowers April–September.

5 **Matricaria tenella** *DC.*
Derivation: Mater (Latin), mother; carus (Latin), esteemed; tenellus (Latin), delicate.
Distribution: Vanrhynsdorp to Malmesbury and Darling.
A small laxly leafy plant. Leaves much divided. Rays white, involucral bracts with membranous margins and tips. Flowers August–October.

6 **Senecio pubigerus** *L.*
Derivation: Senex (Latin), old man (alluding to white hair-like pappus); pubi- (Latin), softly or weakly hairy; -ger (Latin), bearing.
Distribution: Bredasdorp to Clanwilliam.
A perennial, very common. Three or four ray florets. Two or three capitula clustered together. Leaves sessile and decurrent. Flowers March–June.

H mason

PLATE 80 COMPOSITAE

1 **Othonna sonchifolia** DC.

Derivation: Othone (Greek), a linen cloth or napkin (some species have a downy covering); sonchifolius (Latin), with leaves like *Sonchus*, the sow thistle.

Distribution: South western Cape.

An almost stemless plant, with tuberous root. Leaves often succulent and glaucous. About 8 involucral bracts and rays. Flower stalks sometimes purple. Winter flowering.

2 **Othonna quercifolia** DC.

Derivation: Quercifolius (Latin), with leaves like *Quercus*, the oak.

Distribution: Malmesbury, Ceres and Namaqualand.

A small shrub with fleshy leaves and stout succulent stem. Peduncles branching. Only 5–6 involucral bracts. Ripe fruits give appearance of dense off-white woolly heads. Flowers August–September.

3 **Senecio corymbiferus** DC.

Derivation: Senex (Latin), an old man; corymbus (Latin), a corymba, particular arrangement of flower heads; -fer (Latin suffix), bearing.

Distribution: South western Cape to Namaqualand.

Erect, glabrous shrubby succulent with fleshy leaves. Peduncles many-headed. Involucral bracts 8, glabrous. Few small bracts at base. Flowers August–October.

4 **Senecio burchellii** DC.

Derivation: The specific name honours W. J. Burchell, a famous naturalist and traveller who visited the Cape from 1810 to 1815 and wrote a most readable two volume account of "Travels into the interior of South Africa".

Common Name: Geel cineraria.

Distribution: Sandy areas in the south western Cape.

An erect perennial up to 40 cm tall. Leaves half-clasping the stem and toothed at the base. Peduncles nude or sparsely leaved, involucre of about 12 glabrous scales. Like all senecios there are a few small bracts below the involucre. Deadly poisonous to stock. Flowers throughout the year.

5 **Senecio radicans** (L.f.) Schl. Bip.

Derivation: Radicans (Latin), rooting.

Distribution: Widespread throughout South Africa.

Stem prostrate and rooting at intervals. Branches erect and leafy. Leaves fleshy and lanceolate. Heads solitary. Involucral scales linear and pointed. Leaves are eaten by the local inhabitants. Flowers January–June.

6 **Euryops linifolius** DC.

Derivation: Euryops (Greek), having large eyes; linifolius (Latin), flax-leafed.

Distribution: South western Cape.

Leaves simple and narrow. Peduncles bearing the inflorescences, fairly long. Involucral scales joined at the base. 6–8 ray florets. Flowers August–October.

1.

2

3

4

5

6

H Mason

PLATE 81 COMPOSITAE

1 **Helichrysum sesamoides** *Thunb.*
Derivation: Helios (Greek), the sun; chrysos (Greek), gold; sesamoides – like the plant *Sesamum*.
Common Name: Sewejaartjie.
Distribution: South western Cape.
A poorly branched undershrub 40 cm high with slender leafy branches. Leaves round-backed and adpressed to the stem. The flower heads are large, solitary and terminal. Flowers August–December.

2 **Helichrysum stellatum** *Less.*
Derivation: Stellatus (Latin), starry, stellate.
Distribution: From Swellendam to Vanrhynsdorp.
A woolly branched plant, woody at the base. Leaves up to 3 m long, half clasping the stem. Involucral scales in many rows rosy pink with white tips. Flowers September–November.

3 **Helichrysum imbricatum** *Less.*
Derivation: Imbricatus (Latin), imbricate, overlapping.
Distribution: Bredasdorp to Piketberg.
Stems up to 40 cm with spreading branches. Leaves with broad and clasping base. Heads of flowers on branched, leafy stems. The involucral scales are broad, spoon-shaped and brown to horn-coloured. Flowers October–December.

4 **Pteronia divaricata** *Less.*
Derivation: Pteron (Greek), a wing.
Distribution: From Blouberg to Namaqualand.
A small bush, branches twiggy and spreading. Leaves with one prominent vein and often a short apical spine. Flowers June–October.

5 **Senecio scapiflorus** *(L'Her.) C. A. Smith*
Derivation: Senex (Latin), an old man – referring to the white hair-like pappus; scapiflorus (Latin), with flowers up the stem.
Distribution: Namaqualand, Calvinia to Cape Peninsula.
Plants with a basal cluster of leaves, very variable in shape – each with long petiole. Young plants and buds covered with a dense woolly or cobwebby mat. Ray florets absent. Disc florets white with purple anthers and styles. Flowers September–November.

6 **Helipterum variegatum** *DC.*
Derivation: Helios (Greek), the sun; pteron (Greek), a wing.
Common Name: Sewejaartjie.
Distribution: Caledon to Clanwilliam.
Up to 60 cm tall, sparsely branched. Leaves up to 6 cm long and acute – extending to just below the flower head where they are small and tipped with a membranous point forming a transition from the true leaves to involucral bracts. Flower head large and solitary, involucral bracts sometimes tipped with brown. Flowers August–October.

1.

2

3

4

5

6

H mason

PLATE 82 COMPOSITAE

1 **Berkheya rigida** (*Thunb.*) *Bolus & Wolley Dod*
Derivation: Honours Jan de Franq van Berkley, a late 18th century Dutch botanist; rigidus (Latin), rigid.
Common Name: Krammedik.
Distribution: Widespread.
Plants with a milky latex, and rigid spiny leaves and bracts. Florets all tubular. Reputed, in the Darling district, to be a good medicine for stomach complaints. Flowers August–February.

2 **Arctotheca calendula** (*L.*) *Levyns*
Derivation: Arctos (Greek), a bear; theca (Greek), a case; calendulinus (Latin), marigold orange.
Common Name: Cape weed, Cape dandelion.
Distribution: Widespread and naturalised weed in Portugal and Australia.
Involucral bracts in several rows; the inner ones having obtuse membranous tips and outer ones with reflexed tips. Fruits 3–5 ribbed, densely woolly (hence the generic name). Flowers August–November.

3 **Cotula duckittiae** *L. Bolus*
Derivation: Cotule (Greek), a cup. The specific name honours the Duckitt family who for over a hundred years have owned the farm Bokbaai, where they have carefully treasured their floral heritage.
Distribution: Coastal area on Bokbaai and neighbouring farms.
Distinguished from other cotulas by the large head and well developed ray florets. Flowers in September.

4 **Cotula turbinata** *L.*
Derivation: Turbinatus (Latin), top-shaped or obconical.
Common Name: Ganskos.
Distribution: Common in all sandy areas of the west coast in Cape Peninsula. Frequently a weed of cultivation.
A small annual, 5–40 cm tall, hairy. The tip of the peduncle or inflorescence stalk is inflated and hollow below the inflorescence. There are 3 kinds of florets, a marginal one with no corolla, then the florets with the ray-like corolla and finally the tubular disc florets. Flowers June–December.

5 **Cotula coronopifolia** *L.*
Derivation: Coronopifolius (Latin), with leaves like *Coronopus*, the crow foot.
Distribution: Widespread in the Cape especially in damp, flat places.
A creeping annual. The involucral bracts are numerous, outer bracts linear and membranous at the tip. Fruit with a thickened wing, one face smooth and one with short stiff hairs. Flowers May–February.

6 **Erigeron canadense** *L.*
Derivation: Eri (Greek), early; geron (Greek), an old man (inflorescences are fluffy and bearded); canadensis (Latin), of Canada.
Common Name: Peperbos, Skraalhans, Vaalbossie, Vaalknopbos.
Distribution: A weed introduced from North America.
A fairly hairy plant with glabrous involucral bracts. The rays are white and the disc florets yellow. Flowers November–February.

7 **Pteronia uncinata** *DC.*
Derivation: Pteron (Greek), a wing; uncinatus (Latin), hooked.
Distribution: South western Cape.
A shrub 40 cm high. Leaves needle-like. Bracts yellow, innermost ones much shorter than flowers. Flowers December–March.

8 **Matricaria sabulosa** *Wolley Dod*
Derivation: Mater (Latin), mother; carus (Latin), esteemed; sabulosus (Latin), growing in sandy places.
Distribution: Growing near the sea.
A low straggling shrub. Strongly aromatic. Involucral bracts glabrous, obtuse and toothed, often not completely developed at back of flower. Florets all tubular. Flowers September–December.

9 **Conyza ivaefolia** *Less.*
Derivation: Konops (Greek), a gnat; iva – an old generic name of the Compositae; folius – with leaves like –.
Distribution: Widespread in South Africa. Common in bushy areas in the sandveld.
Involucral bracts free, linear to obtuse and glabrous. Marginal florets white, central ones yellow. Flowers December–April.

PLATE 83 COMPOSITAE

1 **Gnaphalium candidissimum** *Lam.*

Derivation: Gnaphalion (Greek), a downy plant; candidus (Latin), glistening, white.

Distribution: South western Cape.

A sprawling herb, probably annual. Capitula in clusters at the tip of the branches, covered with matted woolly substance. Involucral bracts linear; tips spreading; white scarious often emarginate; bases woolly green or reddish. Common. Flowers October–March.

2 **Disparago lasiocarpa** *Cass.*

Derivation: Dispar (Latin), dissimilar; lasiocarpus (Latin), with woolly fruit.

Distribution: South western Cape.

The rays are much longer than the involucral bracts. Only 1–3 flowers in a capitulum. The heads are formed by masses of capitula. Usually pink. Flowers November–March.

3 **Didelta carnosa** *(L. f.) Ait.*

Derivation: Di- (Greek), two; delta, the Greek letter for D; meaning the involucre is double and the involucral bracts are triangular; carnosa (Latin), fleshy.

Common Name: Seegousblom or Duingousblom.

Distribution: Sandveld to Namaqualand.

A glabrous plant with fleshy alternate leaves. 3–5 outer involucral scales are deltoid and the inner ones are sharply pointed. Rays golden-yellow. Grows right down on to the sanddunes. Flowers October–December.

4 **Helichrysum metalasioides** *DC.*

Derivation: Helios (Greek), the sun; chrysos (Greek), gold; metalasioides (Latin), like the genus *Metalasia* (see 5).

Distribution: Frequent in sandy places in the south western Cape.

A perennial with small heath-like leaves. Involucral bracts in several rows are dry, membranous and often brightly coloured. Capitula with only 4–5 flowers. Flowers January–February.

5 **Metalasia imbricata** *Harv.*

Derivation: Meta (Greek), reverse; lasios (Greek), woolly, referring to the leaves; imbricatus (Latin), overlapping.

Distribution: South western Cape.

A South African genus of 33 species. Leaves solitary at nodes in this species, woolly above and glabrous below. Flowers January–March.

6 **Senecio elegans** *L.*

Derivation: Senex (Latin), an old man, alluding to the white hair-like pappus; elegans (Latin), elegant.

Common Name: Wild cineraria.

Distribution: Coastal areas, western to eastern Cape.

A hairy annual which can be up to 1,5 m tall when growing in damp shady places. Plants growing close to the coast look very different from those further inland. The maritime form has thick leaves and is more condensed and hairy. Flowers July–March.

7 **Dimorphotheca pluvialis** *(L.) Moench*

Derivation: Di- (Greek), two; morphe (Greek), form; theca (Greek), a case; referring to the two dissimilar fruits found in many of the species.

Common Name: Witbotterblom, Cape rain daisy.

Distribution: West coast to Cape Peninsula.

A widespread annual sometimes covered with glandular hairs. Leaves often bluntly toothed. Rays white above, biscuit-coloured at the base and purple below. Fruits of the ray florets hard, angular and ridged; disc fruits winged. Flowers July–October.

8 **Stoebe fusca** *(L.) Thunb.*

Derivation: Stoibe (Greek), a shrubby plant used for making brooms and packing wine jars; fuscus (Latin), a sombre brown.

Distribution: Calvinia, Ceres, Malmesbury to Stellenbosch.

A branched shrub 30 cm tall. Leaves heath-like and twisted. Outer involucral scales short and woolly. Only one floret in each capitulum. Flowers March–May.

9 **Stoebe nervigera** *Sch.*

Derivation: Nervus (Latin), a nerve or vein; gero (Latin), I bear.

Distribution: Vanrhynsdorp to Riversdale.

Capitula or heads in small terminal tufts. Leaves keeled and pitted at the back. Involucral scales very pointed. Flowers January–July.

10 **Pteronia onobromoides** *DC.*

Derivation: Pteron (Greek), a wing; onos (Greek), ass; broma (Greek), food. Named after the genus *Onobroma* (Compositae), said to be the favourite food of asses.

Distribution: Saldanha Bay along the coast to Olifants River mouth.

Involucral bracts green. Disc florets only. Heads yellow and aromatic. Leaves with spiny margin. Flowers in November.

1.

2

3

4

5

6

7

8

9

10

H Mason

PLATE 84 COMPOSITAE

1 **Osteospermum fruticosum** *T. Norl.*
Derivation: Osteon (Greek), a bone; sperma (Greek), seed; fruticosus (Latin), shrubby, bushy.
Distribution: Coastal areas.
Stems up to 1 m, trailing on the ground. Leaves tapering at the base. Rays white, reddish or blue beneath. Flowers May–September.

2 **Gazania pectinata** (*Thunb.*) *Spreng.*
Derivation: Gaza (Greek), riches; pectinatus (Latin), pectinate, with narrow close-set divisions like a comb.
Distribution: Bredasdorp, Malmesbury, Graafwater.
Herbaceous, often annual. Basal leaves in a rosette; leaves variable in shape, entire or divided. Involucre glabrous and slightly bristly; lower portion fused and campanulate. Rays yellow to orange, marked with dark brown spots. Flowers most of the year with a peak in spring.

3 **Felicia elongata** (*Thunb.*) *O. Hoffm.*
Derivation: Honours a German officer, Felix; elongatus (Latin), elongated.
Distribution: Saldanha Bay and Langebaan.
An annual. Stem and branches densely hairy. Involucre of usually only one row of bracts. Flower stalks long and hairy. Flowers August–September.

4 **Ursinia anthemoides** (*L.*) *Poir.* ssp. **anthemoides**
Derivation: Honours Johannes Ursinus (1608–1667), the author of Arboretum biblicum, who worked in Regensburg.
Distribution: Melkbosch to Clanwilliam and Calvinia.
An annual up to 50 cm high. Leaves divided, reduced in size at the base of the flowers. Involucre usually lightly pubescent. Rays about 1 cm, rarely longer; yellow and occasionally spotted with deep purple. Flowers September–November.

5 **Arctotheca calendula** (*L.*) *Levyns*
This is a colour variant of the plant illustrated on Plate 82:2.

Didelta carnosa

1

2

3

4

5

H Mason

PLATE 85 COMPOSITAE

1 **Arctotheca populifolia** *(Berg.) T. Norl.*
Derivation: Arctos (Greek), a bear; theka (Greek), a case; populifolius (Latin), with leaves like a poplar.
Distribution: Widespread on the coastal mobile dunes up to Lourenco Marques but not beyond Saldanha on the west coast.
A decumbent herb covered with white wool. Leaves, some simple and ovate and others lobed, are on long petioles. Involucral bracts woolly. Flowers throughout the year.

2 **Charieis heterophylla** *Cass.*
Derivation: Charieis (Greek), elegant; hetero- (Greek), different; uneven; -phyllus (Greek), -leaved.
Common Name: Felicia.
Distribution: Cape Peninsula to Malmesbury and Vanrhynsdorp.
A hairy annual with leaves which vary from lanceolate to oblong. Capitula solitary on long peduncles. Ray florets and disc florets both blue, which distinguishes this from all other Compositae in the south western Cape. Flowers September–October.

3 **Petalacte coronata** *Don.*
Derivation: Petalon (Greek), a petal; aktis (Greek), a ray; coronatus (Latin), crowned.
Distribution: Bredasdorp to Clanwilliam.
A small woody plant, sparsely branched, white–woolly. Heads of flowers small, grouped in large clusters. Leaves and bracts all covered with long woolly hairs. Flowers June–October.

4 **Eriocephalus racemosus** *L.*
Derivation: Erion (Greek), wool; cephale (Greek), head; racemosus (Latin), flowers arranged in a raceme.
Common Name: Kapkappie.
Distribution: Bredasdorp to Piketberg.
Ray florets small and completely hidden in the involucral bracts. Leaves simple; often tufted. Flowers June–September.

5 **Chrysanthemoides monilifera** *(L.) T. Norl.*
Derivation: Like Chrysanthemum; monilifer (Latin), bearing pearls.
Common Name: Bitoubos; Boetabessie.
Distribution: Widespread.
The ripe fruits are fleshy black berries, eaten by birds. Grown successfully along the national roads in the Cape. Flowers throughout the year.

1.

2

3

4

5

Hmason

198

199

201